ADHD
in Love

20 EMOTIONAL REGULATION AND COMMUNICATION
TOOLS TO SAVE YOUR RELATIONSHIP

MAYA BLACKWOOD

Discover the ADHD in Love Workbook!

Enhance your journey with the ADHD in Love workbook, designed to help you apply essential communication and emotional regulation tools in your relationship. Scan the QR code to get started and transform your connection today!

Contents

Introduction

In the complex world of human relationships, the unique trait of attention deficit hyperactivity disorder (ADHD) leaves a distinctive mark. *ADHD in Love: 20 Emotional Regulation and Communication Tools to Save Your Relationship* dives into the deep and often tumultuous different aspects of relationships affected by ADHD, offering tools for understanding.

In my case, the discovery that I have ADHD was a journey of self-reflection that came to life over time. I had always felt that my mind operated in unique ways, often defying conventional structure. However, in my adult life, I began to notice recurring patterns that went beyond simple personality traits.

The difficulties in maintaining concentration on daily tasks, the constant procrastination, and the feeling that my mind was always in a constant swing were signs I could not ignore. My personal and professional relationships were also affected, as impulsivity and lack of organization generated conflicts and misunderstandings.

It was in a time of frustration and searching for answers that I decided to seek guidance from a mental health professional. After careful evaluation, it was confirmed that my experience was aligned with attention deficit hyperactivity disorder. Although initially a daunting discovery, it also represented a crucial turning point.

With the diagnosis in hand, I began to understand my behavioral patterns better and embrace strategies that would allow me to manage my ADHD more effectively. Therapy, support from loved ones, and the implementation of specific tools became fundamental pillars for my adaptation and growth process.

In this introspective journey that the book proposes, I will concisely explain the nature of ADHD and its impact on relationships. From subtle complications to more palpable challenges, we will see how this condition can influence a couple's emotional dynamics. However, this is not a story of hopelessness but a call for understanding and action.

The unwavering need for meaningful connection is at the heart of every relationship. This is where understanding and managing emotional regulation and communication becomes crucial. ADHD can color these areas with unique hues, demanding conscious adaptation to nurture and protect the flame of shared love.

The difficulties for those who have ADHD when relating romantically often manifest themselves in the constant struggle to maintain attention and concentration on the partner. The impulsivity inherent in ADHD can lead to rash decisions or intense emotional expressions, creating volatile terrain in romantic interactions. Furthermore, limited organizational skills and constant distractions can lead to frequent forgetting of commitments or lack of attention in key situations, generating frustration and misunderstandings in the relationship.

On the other hand, those who are in a relationship with someone who has ADHD face unique challenges. The need to understand and adapt to changing behavioral patterns can lead to stress and emotional exhaustion. The lack of structure in the daily life of the partner with ADHD can sometimes lead to the perception of disinterest or carelessness, causing emotional conflicts. Communication can also be difficult, as a racing mind and constant distractions can get in the way of effectively expressing emotions and needs. These difficulties highlight the importance of developing specific and empathic strategies to cultivate successful and satisfying relationships.

Cultivating a positive mentality when facing changes that seek personal improvement and improvement as a human being becomes fundamental in the context of personal relationships. The positive attitude acts as a driving engine that propels the capacity for adaptation and resilience in the face of life's vicissitudes. In the improvement process, the optimistic mind becomes a powerful ally, providing the energy and mental clarity necessary to face challenges with determination and optimism.

Openness to new learning and the willingness to change aspects of oneself to evolve impact the individual and enrich relational dynamics. A positive mindset fosters empathy and understanding, allowing you to better understand the perspectives and needs of others, thus facilitating the construction of stronger and more meaningful bonds.

Furthermore, a positive mindset builds a healthy relational environment where constructive conflict resolution and open communication become possible. Facing changes with an optimistic mindset encourages us to see transformations as opportunities to grow and strengthen, both individually and in the context of relationships. Ultimately, a positive mindset is an essential pillar for facing life's challenges, improving as a human being, and nurturing personal relationships that flourish in authenticity, understanding, and mutual growth.

The experience of having a partner with ADHD can vary significantly depending on the unique dynamics of each relationship and the specific characteristics of ADHD that the person exhibits. However, some common emotions and challenges can arise in these situations.

In many cases, peers may experience frustration due to difficulty maintaining attention and the impulsivity associated with ADHD. Lack of organization and a tendency to be distracted can lead to moments of stress, especially in situations that require planning or focus. A feeling of being misunderstood may also arise, as emotional regulation difficulties and impulsive emotional expression can create misunderstandings in communication.

Additionally, the couple may experience periods of emotional exhaustion, as managing the demands associated with ADHD can be intense and constant. Adjusting to mood swings or the need to provide increased support with everyday tasks can be exhausting. However, it is also possible to experience gratification by observing the moments of creativity, spontaneity, and positive energy that often characterize people with ADHD.

The key in these situations is mutual understanding and finding strategies to manage challenges. Open communication, learning about ADHD, and collaborating on developing strategies for self-regulation can strengthen the relationship. It is important to remember that each person with ADHD is unique, and support and empathy can go a long way toward building a healthy and nurturing relationship.

Within the pages of this book, I'll empower you with a rich array of 20 practical and accessible tools meticulously crafted to fortify emotional resilience and elevate the quality of communication. Each tool will serve as a helpful insight strategically designed to illuminate the path toward cultivating a relationship that not only endures the unique challenges posed by ADHD but emerges stronger and more fulfilling.

These tools are more than just techniques; they represent a comprehensive road map for navigating the complexities of emotional regulation and communication within the context of ADHD-affected relationships. From strategies that foster self-regulation to nuanced approaches that enhance communication dynamics, I invite you to discover and apply these transformative tools.

This journey is an invitation not only to comprehend the intricacies of ADHD but also to actively engage in growth and renewal alongside your partner. Through a harmonious blend of understanding, love, and practical tools, I aim to guide you toward a reborn, resilient, and deeply connected relationship despite the challenges posed by ADHD.

Chapter One

ADHD In Love: 101

You have to be able to slow down enough to switch your focus away from all the ways things could be better to know how good they already are.

–Katherine Ellison

For people living with ADHD, "new love" brings with it a cascade of biochemical euphoria. Despite the intensity of emotions at this stage, it is recognized that these feelings are not enough to build lasting love. It embraces the reality that relationships are complex, challenging the simplistic notion that "all you need is love."

It is understood that coping skills are required to counteract weaknesses and maintain a relationship, especially when it comes to dating someone who has ADHD or having it yourself. The critical question here is what tools should be part of the resource box of an ADHD relationship, remembering that love involves more than simply letting yourself be carried away by momentary feelings (Halverstadt, 2021).

This type of disorder significantly affects personal relationships, manifesting itself through attention challenges, impulsivity, and disorganization. Difficulty concentrating can lead to a lack of attention to essential details for the couple, generating misunderstandings and erroneous perceptions of disinterest. But the important thing about all this is that recognizing your limitations is the first step toward a better relationship.

We are talking about your impulsiveness, which is characterized by quick decisions and interrupted communication. In a relationship, this behavior will only generate tensions and conflicts. The personal disorganization of the individual with ADHD also affects shared daily life, creating a chaotic environment that impacts the stability of the relationship.

This impact is reflected in communication and mutual understanding, which also presents a challenge for those who have ADHD. The difficulty of expressing thoughts coherently and the emotional fluctuations associated with ADHD can lead to misunderstandings and emotional conflicts. A struggle with commitment and responsibility distorts the partner's perception of interest and support. To combat these challenges, education and awareness about ADHD are essential.

In this chapter, we will see how to establish open communication channels and practical strategies, such as implementing routines and reminders. We will try to contribute to mitigating the effects of ADHD on the relationship and make this reading a reference point and source of consultation when you want to improve your life. Ultimately, addressing these challenges holistically strengthens the foundation of the relationship, allowing couples to build a deeper, more lasting understanding of each other.

Think of ADHD in a personal relationship as something similar to preparing for a confrontation with a rival in that fully knowing the nature of the condition is essential. Just as studying your opponent gives you a strategic advantage, understanding the nuances of ADHD allows you to anticipate potential challenges and develop strategies to address them.

ADHD is your opponent in this scenario. However, instead of seeing it as an enemy, it is more beneficial to understand its movements, patterns, and interactions. The key is recognizing that ADHD is not simply a barrier but an intrinsic part of the relationship dynamic.

Knowing your "rival" involves understanding the quirks and challenges of ADHD in the relationship. From impulsiveness to difficulty maintaining attention, each aspect plays a role in the game. As a strategist prepares for the opponent's moves, adapting communication and support strategies is essential in a relationship with ADHD.

Understanding how ADHD influences your actions and reactions can help you approach your relationship with a more compassionate approach. When talking about ADHD and your relationships, the key is not to defeat ADHD but to find ways to coexist and thrive within the relationship.

Decoding ADHD in Relationships

Individuals with ADHD often encounter challenges in sustaining focus on a singular task, which can result in forgetfulness and heightened susceptibility to distractions. In relationships, these difficulties may manifest as forgetfulness regarding significant events, an inability to listen attentively, or an unintended impression of disinterest.

Furthermore, while hyperactivity is commonly linked with ADHD, its manifestation in adults may differ, encompassing restlessness, impulsive decision-making, and a struggle to remain still. In the context of relationships, impulsive actions may lead to misunderstandings, with partners perceiving the individual with ADHD as unpredictable.

Time management poses another hurdle for individuals with ADHD, impacting their adherence to schedules and timelines in relationships. This can elicit frustration from partners who may interpret the struggle as a lack of commitment or responsibility. The communication domain is also affected, as ADHD individuals may frequently interrupt, struggle to maintain focus during conversations, or face challenges expressing thoughts coherently.

Within relationships, these communication difficulties may contribute to misunderstandings, fostering a sense of being unheard or dismissed. Emotional dysregulation, a joint facet of ADHD, introduces mood swings, heightened sensitivity, and difficulties in managing stress. Navigating these emotional highs and lows in relationships demands empathy and the creation of a supportive environment for both partners.

At times, ADHD within my work leads me to thrive under the pressure of imminent deadlines, producing a significant amount of work in a concise span. I become a "master of disasters," effortlessly handling crises while feeling a surge of productivity. Strangely, I seem to be at my best during these chaotic moments.

However, the struggle arises when life returns to its routine pace. Transitioning from one crisis to another becomes a taxing way to go through daily existence. I've noticed a peculiar pattern where the adrenaline rush, essential for my productivity, often relies on tapping into anger. It's as if anger is the catalyst that propels me forward, allowing me to accomplish tasks with a heightened sense of urgency.

Yet, the toll this constant cycle takes on my well-being was undeniable. The steep price paid for productivity raises questions about my mental state—and you have to take care of your mental health. But you'll see that it becomes evident: Lurching from crisis to crisis may yield short-term gains, but the long-term consequences cast a shadow on the sustainability of such a lifestyle (Dodson, 2021).

Emotional Dynamics

ADHD is a neurodevelopmental condition that extends its impact beyond attention and hyperactivity, influencing individuals' emotional regulation. Individuals with ADHD often grapple with intense emotions as a regular part of their daily experience. The relationship between ADHD and emotions is intricate, with many ADHDers experiencing a rapid escalation from zero to 90 in their emotional responses or finding it challenging to bounce back from intense feelings, leading to overthinking that can linger into the night.

As we will see throughout the book, a prominent aspect is impulsivity, where people with ADHD may have difficulty moderating their emotional reactions, responding spontaneously without considering the possible results.

This impulsivity can lead to socially inappropriate emotional expressions, making it difficult for people to regulate their feelings effectively in various situations. It also has to do with the intense emotional response associated with ADHD. This difficulty in measuring emotional reactions is another facet that leads people to experience emotions more intensely than their counterparts without ADHD. This emotional intensity complicates the process of modulating responses, often resulting in emotional outbursts that only negatively influence your personal relationships.

For non-ADHD spouses, this can result in unintentional tuning out of their partners, creating a sense of invalidation. In turn, this mutual invalidation can create emotional distance within the relationship.

Rejection sensitivity adds another layer to the emotional dynamics of ADHD. Many individuals with ADHD report heightened sensitivity to criticism, known as rejection-sensitive dysphoria (RSD). This heightened sensitivity to rejection can make it difficult for individuals to express their needs in relationships and may lead to self-imposed isolation. Despite the desire for connection, those with RSD may struggle to overcome the fear of criticism or rejection, affecting their ability to initiate and maintain relationships over the long term (Roberts, 2022).

People may find it difficult to redirect their attention, which prolongs emotional responses and hinders the ability to overcome intense feelings. Additionally, the disorder can manifest itself in a lower tolerance for frustration, causing people to feel easily overwhelmed by challenges and have difficulty coping with frustration and setbacks in a measured way.

We know that love relationships are complex. They are neither easy nor difficult, just complex. Many variables affect our being, mood, and how we perceive our day. If we add to that complexity a person who struggles to control their emotions and impulsivity, the situation can become an explosive cocktail.

These difficulties often also present as a greater sensitivity to criticism or rejection since people with ADHD can interpret situations as more threatening than they are, amplifying emotional responses disproportionately to the circumstances.

Inconsistent emotional expression in people with ADHD further underscores the challenges they face in regulating their emotions. The struggle to express emotions in a controlled manner can lead to situations where they appear overly emotional or emotionally distant.

While the impact of ADHD on emotion regulation varies among individuals, addressing these challenges often involves a comprehensive approach that incorporates therapeutic interventions, behavioral strategies, and, in some cases, medication. Co-occurring conditions, such as anxiety or depression, can further complicate emotional experiences, highlighting the importance of personalized and targeted interventions to improve emotional regulation in people with ADHD.

Understanding and addressing these emotional dynamics is crucial for both partners in an ADHD-affected relationship. Recognizing the challenges associated with ADHD-related emotions and rejection sensitivity can foster empathy and communication, helping to bridge the gap and build a more supportive and understanding partnership. Seeking professional support, such as therapy, can also be beneficial in navigating these challenges and fostering a healthier emotional connection.

Love and ADHD

Relationships can be challenging in the best of circumstances, but when you are aware of potential ADHD pitfalls, you can take steps to avoid them. The intersection of love and ADHD can present unique challenges and opportunities for individuals navigating relationships. ADHD impacts various aspects of a person's life, including romantic relationships. Understanding how ADHD influences love and intimacy involves recognizing both the potential hurdles and strengths associated with this neurodevelopmental condition.

One notable challenge is the impact of ADHD symptoms on communication within a relationship. Individuals with ADHD may struggle with sustained attention during conversations, leading to misunderstandings or feelings of neglect by their partners. Additionally, impulsivity, a common trait in ADHD, can result in impulsive decision-making or expressions of emotions, which may catch partners off guard. These challenges may require open communication and mutual understanding to navigate successfully.

The foundation of successful relationships hinges on consistently directing our focus and attention toward our partners. Demonstrating care is evident through active interaction, attentive listening, and unwavering support. However, individuals with ADHD often face challenges stemming from symptoms such as inattention, forgetfulness, and disorganization, which can cast a shadow on the relational dynamics. Due to these symptoms, non-ADHD partners may misinterpret their counterparts' intentions, leading to heightened frustration and resentment within the relationship.

ADHD's Pros and Cons in Relationships

It is essential to understand that ADHD in romantic relationships is not inherently good or bad; rather, it represents another variable that influences the dynamics of emotional connection. Embracing this perspective allows us to strip ADHD of stigmas and recognize that, like any other aspect of life, it has its complexities and nuances.

There is no single narrative that defines its impact. On the one hand, ADHD can bring notable advantages, such as boundless creativity, spontaneity, and a vibrant energy that breathes life into the relationship. However, it also poses challenges, such as inattention, forgetfulness, and disorganization, leading to misunderstandings and frustrations.

Adopting a comprehensive view of relationships is essential, recognizing that they are mixed experiences. Just as there are moments of beauty and harmony, there will also be challenging moments. In this context, ADHD becomes one more facet of the complexity inherent in any human relationship. The key lies in embracing the diversity of experiences and appreciating the strengths that ADHD can bring while consciously and collaboratively addressing its challenges.

When we understand that relationships are inherently multifaceted, we can free ourselves from rigid expectations and allow more profound acceptance to flourish. Instead of judging ADHD as a burden or an absolute blessing, we can embrace it as an integral part of the relational experience, recognizing that it contributes to human connections' richness and complexity.

Pros

• **Hyperfocus and Passion**

Individuals with ADHD frequently display a remarkable ability known as hyperfocus, especially in the initial stages of a romantic relationship. This hyperfocus is characterized by intense concentration and dedication to the partner, creating a profound emotional connection.

During this phase, the individual with ADHD devotes undivided attention to their partner, fostering feelings of connection, love, and validation. The passionate focus bestowed upon the partner deepens emotional bonds and contributes to a rapid sense of growth in the relationship. This heightened level of engagement can create a foundation of intimacy and shared experiences that form the bedrock for a solid and meaningful connection.

• **Creativity and Spontaneity**

ADHD individuals bring unique qualities to relationships, including innate creativity and spontaneity. This creativity goes beyond conventional thinking, allowing individuals to generate novel ideas and perspectives. In relationships, this creativity infuses excitement into everyday life.

Partners of individuals with ADHD can expect an ever-evolving dynamic where inventive and unexpected approaches to shared activities disrupt the routine. The ability to think outside the box prevents the relationship from becoming stagnant and opens up opportunities for unique and memorable experiences. This creative energy becomes a driving force that injects vitality into the relationship, making it an engaging and fulfilling journey.

- **Vibrant Energy**

The vibrant energy often associated with individuals with ADHD becomes a potent force within a romantic relationship. This energy is contagious and influences the overall atmosphere of the relationship. Partners benefit from the enthusiasm and liveliness brought into the partnership, creating an enjoyable and engaging dynamic.

The vibrant energy manifests in various ways, from a zest for life to a willingness to explore new possibilities together. It fosters a sense of aliveness and shared adventure, making the relationship a source of companionship and an exciting journey filled with positive energy. The ability to infuse this vibrancy into the relationship contributes to a more fulfilling and dynamic connection between partners.

Cons

- **Lack of Attention**

Attention deficit hyperactivity disorder is a neurodevelopmental disorder characterized by persistent inattention, hyperactivity, and impulsivity patterns. In relationships, inattention can manifest as challenges in maintaining focus on one's partner or relationship dynamics. Individuals with ADHD may experience hyperfocus during the initial stages of a relationship.

This intense focus on their partner can be exhilarating, but it's important to note that this level of attention might not be sustainable in the long term. Over time, the hyperfocus may wane, causing the partner to perceive a sudden loss of interest. This inconsistency can lead to feelings of confusion, uncertainty, and instability in the relationship.

• **Difficulty Concentrating**

When one can't concentrate, it often feels like grasping at scattered thoughts or following a train of thought that constantly derails. It's akin to attempting to focus on a single task while being bombarded by a barrage of distractions. There's a sense of restlessness and frustration as the mind jumps from one idea to another, making it challenging to maintain sustained attention to a specific activity.

Imagine having a mental fog that blurs the clarity of your thoughts, making it difficult to process information or complete tasks efficiently. This can lead to an overwhelmed feeling, as the inability to concentrate can affect productivity and create a sense of being disconnected or disengaged from the present moment.

ADHD often causes difficulty sustaining attention to a particular task or relationship aspect. This can lead to lapses in acknowledging the partner's needs and emotions, creating a sense of neglect. The struggle to stay focused might result in the partner feeling abandoned or emotionally detached. This difficulty in concentrating can erode the emotional connection between individuals, as the non-ADHD partner may interpret the lapses in attention as a lack of care or interest.

• **Impulsivity**

Impulsivity is a hallmark of ADHD, contributing to impulsive decision-making and emotional expression. This can affect various aspects of a relationship, from communication to planning for the future.

Partners may find it challenging to predict or understand the actions and reactions of the individual with ADHD because of impulsivity. This unpredictability can lead to misunderstandings, as impulsive decisions or emotional expressions may not align with the partner's expectations.

Both partners need to work together to navigate the challenges associated with impulsivity. Establishing open communication, setting clear expectations, and developing strategies to manage impulsive behaviors can contribute to a more stable and understanding relationship.

Real Challenges, Real Stories

Part of my journey toward fully understanding this disorder involved dealing with ADHD in a long-term relationship. Then, a few years ago, my partner was diagnosed with ADHD. At first, his hyperfocus was like a spotlight on our relationship, which made me feel incredibly loved. However, as time passed, care inconsistency became a real challenge. It's hard to describe the frustration of feeling like you're talking to someone who is physically there but mentally miles away.

At times, those of us who live with our partner's ADHD have to deal with this horrible feeling as if we do not exist. We look for the other to say something crucial; the lack of attention is total. And let me tell you, you're going to be mad. It is a human and natural reaction to get angry with others without first considering that they are not doing it on purpose. They don't withdraw from the conversation to make you angry; it just happens to them. Sometimes, they are not even aware.

Feeling dismissed or ignored is a lonely place. The turning point for us was seeking help, so I began to educate myself. It was not an instant solution; it took time to read and become aware, and each step forward gave me new tools (some of which I will present here). Over time, it became a resource where we could learn to communicate better.

For example, we set specific times for meaningful conversations and used tools like reminders to stay focused. The agenda on the refrigerator door was crucial. We *all* go to the refrigerator sooner or later. So, it was an excellent place to leave us a message, a reminder, or something that calls us and redirects our attention. Understanding the nature of ADHD brought me a new level of empathy, making me realize that those lapses in attention were unintentional. It has been a journey, but we have traveled it together, hand in hand.

My partner and I also faced this challenge where every disagreement seemed to turn into a storm of emotions, and I was the one causing the thunder. Minor problems escalated, and I could see the impact on the relationship. It was exhausting for everyone, and we decided to seek help through therapy. That decision changed things for us.

Learning about coping mechanisms became essential. Have practical tools to apply daily and dismantle discomforts and fights. We began incorporating breaks during intense discussions and practicing mindfulness techniques. I also worked to identify and express my emotions more clearly. It wasn't an overnight transformation, but gradually, the emotional intensity became more manageable.

Sharing these stories is not easy, but if you are going through similar struggles, I want you to know that you are not alone. Relationships involving ADHD have their unique challenges, but with patience, understanding, and sometimes a little professional guidance, they can become incredibly rewarding. Don't refuse help. You don't have to walk this path completely alone. Remember that progress takes time, willpower, and perseverance when putting your relationship on the best path.

Trust that you can learn and adapt. Every step toward educating yourself about ADHD and understanding how it affects your life and relationships is a step toward empowerment. Don't be discouraged by obstacles. Dealing with ADHD in relationships can be complex, but every little effort counts. Celebrating achievements, no matter how minimal they seem, will remind you of your resilience and ability to overcome challenges. You are the architect of your knowledge and growth.

As we conclude our exploration of the first chapter, we have delved into the intricate dynamics of relationships where ADHD plays a fundamental role. From decoding ADHD in relationships to exploring its emotional impact and weighing the pros and cons, we have embarked on a journey of understanding and empathy.

The biggest takeaway from this chapter is the importance of knowing what attention deficit hyperactivity disorder is all about. The more you know about this disorder, whether you suffer from it or your partner does, the more tools and awareness you will have of how to deal with this issue.

As we turn the page to the next chapter, we will continue our exploration of the challenges ADHD poses in relationships. We will uncover the complexities of communication difficulties resulting from ADHD and explore strategies to overcome misunderstandings. In addition, we will shed light on the concept of neurodiversity in love, offering information about what it means and how it manifests in relationships.

Join us as we explore the beauty of plain old "love" a little differently in the context of neurodiversity. We will provide practical tools tailored to ADHD relationships, offering guidance and support for couples navigating the unique landscape of love in which ADHD plays a role.

Prepare to delve into the complexities of ADHD's impact on your life, discovering ways to foster understanding, connection, and resilience in the face of challenges. The journey continues, and the following chapters promise growth, learning, and a deeper appreciation of the diverse tapestry of love.

Chapter Two

ADHD's Impact On Your Life

The shame that people with ADHD, male or female, carry around with them after years and years of being told that they are inadequate is a critical factor when a marriage starts to fall apart, or when they are approached by a well-meaning spouse about asking for an evaluation for ADHD. Shame often triggers anger and defensiveness, which can shut down what ought to be a straightforward conversation before it has even begun. Anger, stonewalling, and defensiveness can seem unreasonable to a non-ADHD spouse who, not having experienced this same type of repeated bashing of the ego, doesn't understand it or interpret it correctly.

–Melissa Orlov

Navigating life with ADHD is akin to maneuvering through a kaleidoscope of challenges, where the spectrum of impact extends far beyond romantic relationships. As we delve into the intricacies of these issues, it becomes evident that this neurodivergent journey weaves its threads into the very fabric of our daily existence.

The challenges are multifaceted, spanning from the ordinary to the extraordinary. Mundane tasks, which for others may be simple and routine, metamorphose into Herculean feats for those navigating the intricacies of an ADHD mind. For someone with ADHD, this path is fraught with twists and turns, distractions lurking at every corner. The ability to maintain focus and sustain attention becomes a delicate tightrope walk, with the mind often pulled in myriad directions by a chorus of competing thoughts.

As these challenges manifest, time takes on the role of a capricious companion. It slips through our fingers, elusive and unpredictable. The individual with ADHD might find themselves immersed in a task, only to realize that the hours have dissolved like sand slipping through an hourglass. The concept of time becomes both a construct to contend with and a force to reckon with—a source of frustration and, paradoxically, a wellspring of creative spontaneity.

In this dynamic, the organization becomes a constant battle against the chaos ADHD can introduce. The orderly sequence of tasks others may effortlessly follow becomes a puzzle with scattered pieces. Creating and adhering to routines can be a formidable task, and the simple act of planning may feel like attempting to grasp a handful of scattered leaves in the gust of wind.

The impact extends beyond the practicalities; it seems into the emotional landscape. Frustration, self-doubt, and an overwhelmed sense become companions on this journey. However, within this labyrinth of challenges lies an opportunity for growth and resilience. As individuals with ADHD develop coping mechanisms and strategies, they discover a unique path through the maze—one that might not follow a straight line but can be rich with unexpected discoveries and insights.

When you take these issues to everyday responsibilities, the individual with ADHD is not just a navigator but an adventurer, facing challenges that forge character, determination, and creativity. It's a journey where each twist and turn is an opportunity to uncover strengths and embrace the dynamic, ever-evolving nature of life with ADHD.

Yet, it's not merely about the external challenges; the internal landscape is equally profound. The ADHD mind, with its perpetual dance of ideas and thoughts, can be both a source of creativity and a tumultuous sea of distraction. The quest for sustained focus and executive functioning is a quest for equilibrium in a world that often demands conformity to linear thinking.

In facing these challenges, cultivating the right mindset becomes paramount. A mindset that embraces neurodiversity as a unique tapestry of strengths and challenges, recognizing that the rhythm of an ADHD mind can compose symphonies of innovation. It's about embracing imperfection and understanding that progress, not perfection, is the beacon guiding this journey.

Furthermore, ADHD's impact transcends the individual, reverberating through relationships, work, and personal fulfillment. Communication difficulties may arise, but with patience and understanding, bridges can be built. The key lies in fostering an environment of open dialogue, where partners, colleagues, and friends learn to navigate the ebbs and flows of ADHD dynamics.

ADHD invites a unique perspective, a lens through which the world is seen in black and white and in a myriad of vibrant hues. The impulsive spark of creativity, the ability to hyperfocus with unwavering intensity, and the resilience born from overcoming constant hurdles are treasures embedded in the ADHD experience.

In this chapter, we'll unravel the layers of this intricate tapestry. From challenges to shifts in mindsets and the profound impact on daily existence, we embark on a journey of self-discovery and understanding. It's an odyssey that invites acceptance, resilience, and an appreciation for the kaleidoscope of experiences that make up life with ADHD.

In the complex world of human relationships, the unique trait of attention deficit hyperactivity disorder (ADHD) leaves a distinctive mark. *ADHD in Love: 20 Emotional Regulation and Communication Tools to Save Your Relationship* dives into the deep and often tumultuous different aspects of relationships affected by ADHD, offering tools for understanding.

In my case, the discovery that I have ADHD was a journey of self-reflection that came to life over time. I had always felt that my mind operated in unique ways, often defying conventional structure. However, in my adult life, I noticed recurring patterns beyond simple personality traits.

The difficulties in maintaining concentration on daily tasks, the constant procrastination, and the feeling that my mind was always in a constant swing were signs I could not ignore. My personal and professional relationships were also affected, as impulsivity and lack of organization generated conflicts and misunderstandings.

It was in a time of frustration and searching for answers that I decided to seek guidance from a mental health professional. After careful evaluation, it was confirmed that my experience was aligned with attention deficit hyperactivity disorder. Although initially a daunting discovery, it also represented a crucial turning point.

With the diagnosis in hand, I began to understand my behavioral patterns better and embrace strategies that would allow me to manage my ADHD more effectively. Therapy, support from loved ones, and the implementation of specific tools became fundamental pillars for my adaptation and growth process.

In this introspective journey that the book proposes, I will concisely explain the nature of ADHD and its impact on relationships. We will see how this condition can influence a couple's emotional dynamics, from subtle complications to more palpable challenges. However, this is not a story of hopelessness but a call for understanding and action.

The unwavering need for meaningful connection is at the heart of every relationship. This is where understanding and managing emotional regulation and communication becomes crucial. ADHD can color these areas with unique hues, demanding conscious adaptation to nurture and protect the flame of shared love.

The difficulties for those who have ADHD when relating romantically often manifest themselves in the constant struggle to maintain attention and concentration on the partner. The impulsivity inherent in ADHD can lead to rash decisions or intense emotional expressions, creating volatile terrain in romantic interactions. Furthermore, limited organizational skills and constant distractions can lead to frequent forgetting of commitments or lack of attention in key situations, generating frustration and misunderstandings in the relationship.

On the other hand, those who are in a relationship with someone who has ADHD face unique challenges. Understanding and adapting to changing behavioral patterns can lead to stress and emotional exhaustion. The lack of structure in the daily life of the partner with ADHD can sometimes lead to the perception of disinterest or carelessness, causing emotional conflicts. Communication can also be difficult, as a racing mind and constant distractions can get in the way of effectively expressing emotions and needs. These difficulties highlight the importance of developing specific and empathic strategies to cultivate successful and satisfying relationships.

Cultivating a positive mentality when facing changes that seek personal improvement and improvement as a human being becomes fundamental in the context of personal relationships. The positive attitude acts as a driving engine that propels the capacity for adaptation and resilience in the face of life's vicissitudes. In the improvement process, the optimistic mind becomes a powerful ally, providing the energy and mental clarity necessary to face challenges with determination and optimism.

Openness to new learning and the willingness to change aspects of oneself to evolve impact the individual and enrich relational dynamics. A positive mindset fosters empathy and understanding, allowing one to better understand the perspectives and needs of others, thus facilitating the construction of stronger and more meaningful bonds.

Furthermore, a positive mindset builds a healthy relational environment where constructive conflict resolution and open communication become possible. Facing changes with an optimistic mindset encourages us to see transformations as opportunities to grow and strengthen, both individually and in the context of relationships. Ultimately, a positive mindset is essential for facing life's challenges, improving as a human being, and nurturing personal relationships that flourish in authenticity, understanding, and mutual growth.

The experience of having a partner with ADHD can vary significantly depending on the unique dynamics of each relationship and the specific characteristics of ADHD that the person exhibits. However, some common emotions and challenges can arise in these situations.

In many cases, peers may experience frustration due to difficulty maintaining attention and the impulsivity associated with ADHD. Lack of organization and a tendency to be distracted can lead to stress, especially in situations that require planning or focus. A feeling of being misunderstood may also arise, as emotional regulation difficulties and impulsive emotional expression can create misunderstandings in communication.

Additionally, the couple may experience periods of emotional exhaustion, as managing the demands associated with ADHD can be intense and constant. Adjusting to mood swings or the need to provide increased support with everyday tasks can be exhausting. However, it is also possible to experience gratification by observing the moments of creativity, spontaneity, and positive energy that often characterize people with ADHD.

The key in these situations is mutual understanding and finding strategies to manage challenges. Open communication, learning about ADHD, and collaborating on developing self-regulation strategies can strengthen the relationship. It is important to remember that each person with ADHD is unique, and support and empathy can go a long way toward building a healthy and nurturing relationship.

Within the pages of this book, I'll empower you with a rich array of 20 practical and accessible tools meticulously crafted to fortify emotional resilience and elevate the quality of communication. Each tool will serve as a helpful insight strategically designed to illuminate the path toward cultivating a relationship that not only endures the unique challenges posed by ADHD but emerges stronger and more fulfilling.

These tools are more than just techniques; they represent a comprehensive road map for navigating the complexities of emotional regulation and communication within the context of ADHD-affected relationships. From strategies that foster self-regulation to nuanced approaches that enhance communication dynamics, I invite you to discover and apply these transformative tools.

This journey is an invitation to comprehend the intricacies of ADHD and actively engage in growth and renewal alongside your partner. Through a harmonious blend of understanding, love, and practical tools, I aim to guide you toward a reborn, resilient, and deeply connected relationship despite the challenges posed by ADHD.

Challenges in ADHD Relationships

Neurodiverse romantic relationships, which include couples with diverse neurological profiles such as autism, ADHD, dyslexia, and more, make up about 15%–20% of the population. In these relationships, common sources of conflict often arise from difficulties in understanding how each partner processes information (Renteria, 2024).

The first significant challenge arises in communication, where misinterpretations are amplified due to differences in information processing. Mind reading and jumping to conclusions becomes more pronounced, making it likely that one or both partners will misunderstand each other. This dynamic contributes to a pervasive feeling of being misunderstood, with neurotypical individuals perceiving a lack of effort on the part of their neurodivergent counterparts and neurodivergent couples feeling that their loved ones lack the necessary patience or understanding.

The second challenge involves defensiveness or the perception of being defensive, which is common in neurodiverse couples. Different perspectives on what is acceptable within the relationship can create a constant need for explanation, leading to hypervigilance, guilt, and shame.

This deadlock in communication creates a dynamic where both partners feel nervous whenever conflicts arise. Additionally, neurotypical partners may have difficulty overlooking differences and maintaining expectations that their neurodivergent partners process information similarly.

The key to thriving in neurodiverse relationships lies in changing the narrative. Understanding and respecting differences in information processing is crucial. Seeking professional guidance can help you understand these distinctions and set realistic expectations.

Collaboratively taking inventory of everyday struggles, working on precise, non-defensive communication, and addressing sensory issues contribute to building resilience and intimacy. By embracing differences and encouraging open communication, neurodiverse relationships have the potential to not only survive challenges but also flourish (Renteria, 2024).

Creativity With ADHD

Listen to anyone with an original idea, no matter how absurd it may sound at first. If you put fences around people, you get sheep. Give people the room they need. –William McKnight

Creativity is a distinctive characteristic of people with ADHD. This creativity can manifest in various ways, from innovative approaches to solving problems to generating fresh and original ideas. Creativity can be a valuable asset in a relationship, bringing dynamism and vitality to everyday life. Thinking outside the box can inspire new activities, projects, and perspectives, adding a unique touch to the relationship. The couple can enjoy the adventure of exploring different ideas and experiences, making the relationship more exciting and enriching.

Additionally, the "wit" associated with ADHD can play a crucial role in positive thinking within the relationship. Here, ingenuity refers to finding creative solutions to everyday challenges.

Instead of seeing ADHD as a limitation, it can be used as an engine to develop innovative strategies and adapt to changing circumstances. For example, establishing structured routines with a creative touch and incorporating interesting elements can make daily activities more attractive and manageable.

The couple can learn to appreciate and encourage this "resourcefulness" when facing difficult situations. Instead of focusing on challenges alone, you can work together to identify creative solutions and flexible approaches. The positive attitude toward creativity associated with ADHD can become a powerful asset, strengthening the relationship by allowing both partners to explore new perspectives and find unique ways to approach the complexities of daily life.

ADHD-Related Communication Difficulties

Communication forms the basis of any relationship and serves as a bridge that connects people emotionally, intellectually, and socially. However, when ADHD is involved, this bridge can face unique challenges, introducing a layer of nuance to the dynamics of interpersonal connection.

One of the most critical obstacles in relationships with ADHD is communication difficulties. The ADHD mind, characterized by its rapid thoughts, may sometimes have trouble maintaining a constant, focused dialogue. Conversations can become a whirlwind of ideas, making it difficult for people with ADHD to convey their thoughts coherently.

The inclination to become easily distracted poses a formidable challenge in effective communication. When engaged in a simple discussion, external stimuli or internal thoughts have the potential to divert attention, leading to a cascade of complications. This diversion can act as a disruptive force, derailing the flow of the conversation and impeding the smooth exchange of ideas.

For instance, the ubiquity of smartphones and other electronic devices introduces a constant stream of potential diversions. Notifications, messages, and the lure of digital content can all serve as disruptive elements that fragment the focus of those engaged in conversation.

Moreover, internal distractions, such as daydreaming, preoccupation with personal concerns, or a wandering mind, can also contribute to the breakdown of effective communication. In such instances, one or both partners may find it challenging to remain fully present and attentive, feeling unheard or misunderstood. This lack of engagement can erode the foundation of a meaningful conversation, leaving individuals frustrated and communication objectives unmet.

To mitigate the impact of distractions on communication, individuals may consider implementing strategies to enhance focus and presence during discussions. These strategies could include creating a conducive environment free from unnecessary interruptions, practicing mindfulness techniques to anchor attention to the present moment, and establishing explicit communication norms with conversation partners.

Recognizing and addressing the tendency to be easily distracted is crucial for fostering healthy and productive communication. By doing so, individuals can cultivate a more focused and attentive approach to conversations, ultimately minimizing the risk of breakdowns and ensuring that messages are conveyed and received with clarity and understanding.

Responses may be blurted out without proper consideration, which could lead to misunderstandings or unintentional hurt feelings. It is not uncommon for people with ADHD to have to deal with the consequences of words spoken in the heat of the moment, reflecting the impulsive nature of their cognitive processes.

In relationships where one partner has ADHD and the other does not, a gap in communication styles can arise. The partner without ADHD may have difficulty keeping up with rapid changes in conversation or may find it challenging to decipher the underlying intentions behind impulsive statements. This disconnection can create a sense of frustration and may require a deliberate effort from both partners to close the communication gap.

Addressing communication difficulties related to ADHD involves fostering understanding and empathy. Both partners can work together to establish effective communication strategies, such as setting clear expectations for conversations, practicing active listening, and implementing structured communication techniques. Additionally, cultivating an open, non-judgmental space allows both people to express themselves authentically, fostering a more profound connection despite the challenges that ADHD poses.

Delineating the complex edges of communication within ADHD relationships requires patience, flexibility, and a commitment to mutual growth. Recognizing and addressing these challenges head-on is crucial; couples can build a foundation that withstands the unique complexities of ADHD-related communication difficulties, fostering a relationship characterized by understanding and resilience.

Overcoming ADHD-Related Misunderstandings

Living with ADHD can present unique communication challenges that, if not addressed, can lead to frequent misunderstandings in various aspects of life. Overcoming misunderstandings related to ADHD requires a collaborative effort from both people with ADHD and their partners, friends, or colleagues.

A common source of misunderstanding arises from the rapid and often divergent flow of thoughts in the ADHD mind. This can lead to conversations that take unexpected turns, leaving others confused or feeling unheard. To address this, people with ADHD can practice implementing communication strategies, such as summarizing key points during discussions or using visual aids to improve clarity.

Another challenge arises from the tendency toward impulsive responses, in which words may be spoken without thorough consideration. Partners and friends can play a supportive role by recognizing this trait and, in times of stress, allowing a pause for reflection before responding. Implementing the practice of breathing and considering responses can significantly help reduce misinterpretations.

Rejection sensitivity dysphoria, a common aspect of ADHD, adds another layer to the misunderstandings. People with ADHD may perceive rejection in even minor interactions, leading to defensive reactions. Open and empathetic communication is essential here. Partners and friends can express understanding and reassurance, fostering an environment where people with ADHD feel safe expressing themselves without fear of judgment.

Establishing clear expectations and open channels for dialogue is crucial to overcoming misunderstandings. Both parties must feel comfortable expressing their perspectives, acknowledging differences, and working collaboratively to find solutions. Regular check-ins can serve as opportunities to address lingering concerns or clarify points of contention, contributing to a healthier, more dynamic understanding.

Next, we will see the five most common myths about this type of disorder and the importance of knowing this information to improve personal relationships:

• *Myth 1: ADHD Is Not a Real Disorder*

Contrary to the belief that ADHD is not a legitimate disorder, historical records and over 10,000 scientific publications affirm its reality. Research highlights stark differences between individuals with and without ADHD, impacting social, emotional, academic, and work functioning. It is hereditary, with a 57% chance for a child if a parent has ADHD. Brain scans reveal distinct developmental differences in individuals with ADHD (Barkley, 2015).

• Myth 2: ADHD Is a Disorder of Childhood

ADHD is not confined to childhood; it persists into adolescence (50%–80% of cases) and adulthood (35%–65% of cases). Long-term studies indicate that ADHD is a lifespan disorder, challenging the notion that it naturally wanes with age (Owens, 2015).

• Myth 3: ADHD Is Over-Diagnosed

While the diagnosed rate in children has increased, it doesn't necessarily indicate over-diagnosis. Healthcare practitioners follow best practice guidelines, and increased awareness, screenings, and decreased stigma contribute to higher diagnostic rates. Environmental factors may also play a role (Visser, 2015).

• Myth 4: Children With ADHD Are Over-Medicated

Research suggests that ADHD is either appropriately treated or under-treated. Medication is not excessive, with only 69% of diagnosed children taking medication. Prevalence rates and treatment data indicate a balanced approach rather than over-medication (*Myths and Misunderstandings*, 2018).

• Myth 5: Poor Parenting Causes ADHD

Genetic and neurological factors, not poor parenting, are the leading causes of ADHD. Family environments contribute minimally to ADHD symptoms, although parenting practices can affect coexisting disorders. ADHD is rooted in heredity and neurological factors, dispelling the notion that it stems from parenting practices (Barkley, 2015).

Neurodiversity in Love

People with ADHD often have a special feel for life, a way of seeing right into the heart of matters, while others have to reason their way methodically.

–Dr. Edward M. Hallowell

Dr. Edward M. Hallowell illuminates the unique perspective that individuals with ADHD bring to life. He emphasizes that those with ADHD often possess an intuitive understanding, a unique "feel" for things that allow them to grasp the essence of matters without the need for systematic reasoning.

This insight resonates with the concept of neurodiversity, which recognizes and celebrates the diverse ways in which individuals' brains function. Neurodiversity acknowledges that neurological differences, such as ADHD, are natural variations of the human experience rather than disorders that need fixing.

Understanding and appreciating this neurodiversity is crucial for fostering inclusivity and empathy. It prompts us to recognize that there isn't a one-size-fits-all approach to experiencing and navigating the world. Instead, different perspectives and ways of processing information contribute to the richness of human existence.

Neurodiversity in love explores the multifaceted and enriching dynamics that arise when individuals with diverse neurological profiles engage in romantic relationships.

In neurodiverse relationships, the traditional norms of love are redefined. It's about recognizing and celebrating the intricate threads of diversity woven into the fabric of the partnership. Each neurological difference becomes a unique hue, contributing to the overall richness and complexity of the connection. It's an invitation to move beyond societal expectations and embrace the authentic expression of love that emerges when individuals with varying neurological perspectives come together.

The journey of neurodiversity in love involves understanding that there is no one-size-fits-all approach. Instead, it encourages an appreciation for how individuals process information and experience the world. Challenges become opportunities for growth and understanding, fostering a relationship dynamic that thrives on acceptance and resilience.

Ultimately, it's not just about acceptance; it's about active celebration. It's an ongoing exploration marked by mutual understanding, continuous growth, and unwavering support. As partners traverse this path together, they discover that their differences are not obstacles but rather the building blocks of a relationship that is not just different but uniquely beautiful and resilient.

What Do We Mean by "Neurodiversity"?

Neurodiversity should be conceived as a vibrant celebration of the diversity inherent in the human mind. When applied to the realm of love and relationships, this concept takes on a profound transformative meaning. It underscores the idea that conditions like autism, ADHD, dyslexia, and others offer unique and valuable perspectives that enrich the shared journey of partnership.

In the relationship landscape, embracing neurodiversity goes beyond mere acceptance; it demands a genuine celebration of the distinctive qualities that neurodivergent individuals bring to the table. Each neurodivergent trait contributes to the kaleidoscope of human experience, offering a wealth of insights, creativity, and approaches that can enhance the depth and resilience of relationships.

Neurodiversity in relationships encourages an open-minded exploration of communication styles, emotional expressions, and problem-solving methods. It encourages partners to move away from conventional norms and appreciate the beauty of diverse cognitive processes.

Additionally, celebrating neurodiversity in relationships is a call to dismantle stereotypes and misconceptions surrounding neurodivergent conditions. It challenges preconceived notions and encourages a shift toward a more inclusive and compassionate understanding of the diverse ways in which individuals experience and express love.

Plain Old "Love," Just a Little Different

Love, in its purest form, remains a timeless and universal experience, yet within the realm of neurodiverse relationships, it takes on a distinctive hue. The simplicity of love endures, but the intricacies become more pronounced. The perception of the concept of "love" can be intense and passionate for people with ADHD, who tend to experience emotions deeply. Their impulsive nature can lead to spontaneous displays of affection, and their commitment can be vibrant when they are focused on the relationship. However, fluctuating attention and changing interests can influence how they express and experience love, sometimes constantly seeking novelty and excitement in the relationship.

Additionally, challenges in organization and planning can affect the execution of romantic gestures, but this does not necessarily reflect a lack of love. Open communication, empathy, and acceptance of individual differences are essential to understanding and appreciating the rich complexity of the perception of love in people with ADHD.

Communication, understanding, and the nuanced dance of emotions require an extra layer of patience and empathy. It's a unique love that transcends conventional norms, demanding a profound understanding of each partner's distinctive perspective and a heightened level of compassion. In neurodiverse love, the ordinary becomes extraordinary as partners navigate the complexities of their unique connection.

Practical Tools for ADHD Relationships

Not enough people realize that ADHD is not a disorder about loss of focus. It is a disorder of loss of emotional control, which is triggered by outside influences, self-esteem, and our interpretation of events. Whether this is positive or negative, it triggers us to hyper-focus on what consumes our thoughts. Staying positive is critical, and distancing oneself from hurtful people is essential, in order to live a life with purpose.

–Shannon L. Alder

The positive impact of practical tools on relationships affected by ADHD goes beyond solving daily problems, reaching a fundamental emotional dimension: self-confidence. People dealing with ADHD often face challenges ranging from organization to time management, and these obstacles can affect their self-image and self-esteem.

Practical tools offer tangible solutions to these difficulties and act as catalysts to strengthen confidence in one's ability to face and overcome challenges.

The successful implementation of specific strategies provides individuals with a sense of achievement, demonstrating that they can positively influence their environment and, therefore, their relationships. This gradual process of building trust contributes not only to improving the quality of life of the individual with ADHD but also to consolidating a more positive and resilient self-image.

Incorporating practical tools to address my partner's ADHD was transformative for me. Seeing the positive impact of these tools on daily life and the emotional dynamics of the relationship generated a sense of trust and collaboration that was essential in overcoming obstacles and building a stronger connection. These concrete strategies strengthened our communication and mutual understanding.

Furthermore, the impact extends to the relationship itself. The newly acquired confidence of the individual with ADHD translates into greater openness and participation in the relationship, strengthening the emotional connection with their partner.

As partners witness the advancements and effectiveness of practical tools, an environment of mutual understanding and collaboration is created, thus promoting a shared sense of overcoming challenges.

The resulting mutual trust improves the relationship dynamics and fosters a space where both partners feel safe expressing their needs and working together toward mutually beneficial solutions.

This trust contributes to the construction of more solid and empathetic relationships, where overcoming challenges becomes a shared effort and a catalyst for emotional growth and stability in the couple.

In this chapter, we have delved into the complex and diverse impact of ADHD on our lives, exploring the nuances of its personal and emotional effects. We have recognized the challenges that arise, from concentration difficulties to emotional ups and downs, and have highlighted the importance of maintaining a positive and confident attitude in facing these obstacles.

That's what this path is about: being able to be better ourselves to improve our environment and the people around us. When your partner has ADHD, you know that a part of you must adjust. You do it for love, and you positively change their lives. Because you understand ADHD as a part of them, and you see it as something you can also learn from.

When we better understand and interpret how ADHD influences our daily lives, we have laid the foundation for the crucial next step: applying specific tools designed to address these challenges effectively. We have highlighted the relevance of these tools as practical guides that will help manage the most challenging aspects of ADHD and transform our relationship with this disorder.

These strategies seek to infuse creativity into the approach to life with ADHD, turning learning and adaptation into shared and stimulating experiences. Incorporating fresh and creative approaches addresses practical difficulties and strengthens the emotional bond, turning challenges into opportunities to grow together innovatively.

• Interactive Educational Navigation

This transforms the understanding of ADHD into a joint and dynamic experience. They engage in interactive educational activities that address ADHD from playful perspectives, such as personalized board games or interactive apps. This approach will not only educate but also encourage communication in creative ways. Imagine creating an "ADHD map" visually representing challenges and successes, providing a unique way to explore and understand your partner's experience.

• Choreography of Time

Put a creative spin on daily routines and structures. Think of everyday life as a choreography of time, where every movement is carefully designed. Together, they co-create a unique "choreography" for everyday life, allocating specific times for key tasks and creating rituals that provide a harmonious flow. This creative perspective provides structure and turns daily responsibilities into a collaborative dance.

- **Empathy and Resilience Game**

Transform the cultivation of empathy and resilience into a collaborative game. Create cards or challenges encouraging empathy, such as "Put yourself in someone else's shoes" or "Find the silver lining in a challenging situation." This playful approach makes empathy more tangible and turns resilience into a strategic game. Find innovative ways to face challenges, stimulating creativity and adaptability in the relationship.

In the next chapter, we take the talk to the realm of reality. We'll dive right into what brought you here: the 20 best tools for dealing with ADHD. We begin a learning journey in which we will explore in detail these practical and useful tools designed to integrate into our daily lives. These tools will be valuable allies for a more balanced and fulfilling life.

It is essential to remember that this learning path can be challenging and requires effort and dedication. However, if you are here, reading these words, you already have what it takes to face this challenge with determination and resilience.

So, onto the next stage: Let's get those tools!

Chapter Three

Building Empathy and Compassion

Some people with ADHD compensated for their ADHD in childhood but fall apart after they have too much on their plate as adults. Typically, this happens with the introduction of children into your lives. Raising kids takes an inordinate amount of organizational skill, which is not generally an ADHD strong point.

–Melissa Orlov

L iving with ADHD presents unique obstacles in several aspects of life, from managing time and tasks to maintaining focus and regulating emotions. These challenges can often be misinterpreted or overlooked by those who do not experience them firsthand, leading to frustration and strained relationships. However, by cultivating empathy and compassion, we can bridge the gap between different perspectives and foster a deeper understanding of the experiences and needs of people with ADHD.

This chapter will explore the first and perhaps most critical practical strategies and tools for promoting empathy and compassion in various contexts. Everything we will achieve from now on is based on daily and constant empathy.

Everything begins here, and incorporating these three essential tools is a high priority. To truly improve the lives of people with ADHD, you must feel like them. You must put yourself in their shoes, understand their challenges, and accompany them to celebrate their results. You must have enough empathy and compassion to actively recognize that "extra" effort that everyday life takes.

To do this, we will analyze it together. From communication techniques that encourage active listening and validation to mindfulness practices that improve awareness and emotional regulation, we will discover ways to cultivate empathy toward others and ourselves.

Additionally, we will discuss the importance of fostering compassion in relationships affected by ADHD. It's about recognizing the inherent difficulties of living with ADHD and offering support without judgment. Encourage partners, family, and friends to create a nurturing environment for people with ADHD to thrive.

In this journey of creating empathy and compassion, let us remember that the final goal is to achieve a state of comprehensive well-being for all those involved in the relationship. Together, let's pave the way for deeper connections, mutual respect, and a greater sense of unity in our ADHD-affected relationships.

Tool 1: Empathy

Dealing with a romantic relationship with a partner who has ADHD requires the essential tool of empathy. Being empathetic toward your partner, especially with ADHD, involves diving deeply into their experiences and challenges. It is an active commitment to understanding the specific symptoms of ADHD and how it affects your loved one's daily life.

Empathy manifests itself through active listening, validating your emotions, and showing unconditional support, free of judgment. Putting yourself in your partner's shoes means imagining the world from their unique perspective and recognizing the influence of ADHD on their decisions and behaviors. Furthermore, empathy implies understanding and collaborating to find solutions and celebrate achievements together, thus creating an environment of understanding and mutual support in the relationship.

Evolution of Empathy and Compassion

The evolution of empathy and compassion in humans has been a crucial phenomenon that has shaped not only our interpersonal relationships but also social cohesion and, ultimately, the survival of the species. Over millennia, these capabilities have proven to be fundamental features of our nature and essential elements that have conferred notable adaptive advantages on humanity.

The emergence of empathy and compassion in humans can be traced back to the dawn of social existence. As our early ancestors began to live in larger communities, the ability to understand and share the emotions of others became invaluable. These skills promoted social cohesion and strengthened community ties, providing an adaptive advantage by increasing collaboration and cooperation.

Empathy and compassion facilitated cooperation between individuals within social groups. These feelings generated a willingness to help others, share resources, and collaborate on everyday tasks. Forming more robust social bonds improved the quality of life within communities. It increased the ability to confront external challenges, such as foraging, defending against predators, and resolving conflict.

Empathy and compassion played a crucial role in developing communication and conflict resolution. The ability to understand the emotions and perspectives of others allowed our ancestors to anticipate and address interpersonal tensions. The peaceful resolution of conflicts within social groups promoted stability and harmony, essential for addressing environmental challenges and ensuring continued survival.

As social complexity evolved, empathy and compassion drove cognitive and cultural development. The ability to understand and share emotional experiences contributed to language development and knowledge transmission between generations. Empathy was also a catalyst for forming ethical norms and value systems, strengthening social cohesion and cultural identity.

These capabilities not only improved the quality of social interactions but also provided adaptive advantages crucial to the survival and flourishing of our species.

Empathy in ADHD Love

Empathy in a relationship with a partner dealing with ADHD also requires continued patience. Understand that managing this condition is a constantly evolving process, and be willing to offer the time and space necessary to overcome obstacles and learn to manage ADHD. Celebrating each step, no matter how small, strengthens the emotional connection and builds a solid and healthy relationship based on mutual understanding and constant support.

For starters, gaining a deeper understanding of ADHD involves continuing education. Read literature, attend seminars, or consult professionals to understand the complexities of ADHD. This knowledge provides insight and demonstrates a commitment to understanding your partner's unique experiences.

Active listening, which we discussed previously, means going beyond just listening to words. It involves immersing yourself in your partner's narrative, absorbing the emotions behind their words, acknowledging their struggles, and validating your experiences with them. The empathic connection will improve thanks to the improvement of the couple's communication spaces.

Implementing practical strategies to incorporate empathy into a relationship with your partner with ADHD is essential to strengthening the emotional connection and promoting a supportive environment:

- The first strategy highlights the importance of creating an open, judgment-free communication space. Inviting your partner to share their experiences, whether challenges or achievements, without fear of criticism lays the foundation for mutual acceptance and understanding. During difficult conversations, offering unconditional support reinforces empathy, thus building a safe environment where you can express your thoughts and feelings honestly.

- The second strategy focuses on the structuring of specific communication routines. Recognizing the importance of communication in an ADHD relationship, scheduling regular times to discuss concerns, accomplishments, and necessary adjustments provides a structure that facilitates openness and mutual understanding. These routines offer predictability, promoting anticipation and active engagement in conversations, which contributes to an environment of empathy and understanding.

- The third strategy focuses on creating discrete cues or cue words as gentle reminders during specific ADHD-related situations. These signals are tangible manifestations of support and understanding, offering a silent reminder that you are present and willing to support your partner in times of distraction or frustration. These practices strengthen the emotional bond, thus consolidating empathy in the relationship.

Together, these strategies establish a solid foundation for empathy in an ADHD relationship and also foster an environment where both partners feel heard, understood, and supported, contributing to the couple's health and emotional stability.

The Dual Nature Between Empathy and Rejection Sensitive Dysphoria (RSD)

One of the most significant advantages of people with ADHD is their immense capacity for empathy. They are exceptional at empathizing with others, making them great friends in social relationships. Likewise, in romantic relationships, that remarkable gift of putting yourself in another's shoes gives you an advantage when deciphering unexpressed emotions and connecting deeply with others.

People with ADHD have an intuitive understanding of the feelings of others that often position them as pillars of support in their relationships. This is due to their deep empathy. In these cases, they are experts at providing unparalleled comfort and companionship, whether guiding a child through the anxieties of the first day of school or offering encouragement to a colleague before a pivotal presentation. These empathetic qualities inherent in ADHD can be celebrated as the cornerstone of meaningful connections.

However, despite their remarkable empathic abilities, some people with ADHD experience the other side of their emotional sensitivity: distressing rejection-sensitive dysphoria.

We are talking about an intense emotional response that arises from the perceived feeling of rejection or criticism from essential people in their lives. I say "perceived" because that sensation is very personal and may or may not have concrete foundations in reality. Sometimes, this phenomenon can make people with ADHD feel rejection or criticism when, in fact, that was not the case. Therefore, RSD can be accurately characterized as "extreme emotional sensitivity and pain" (Hallowell, 2021).

Understanding RSD

Describing the distress associated with rejection sensitivity represents a significant challenge for those who experience RSD. The emotions linked to this phenomenon manifest with an intensity often difficult to express in words—overwhelming, intense, and omnipresent feelings.

There is a need, in these cases, for someone to encourage people to recognize that perceived rejections may have no basis in reality. The vivid imagination that characterizes those with RSD can trigger feelings of rejection that are ultimately baseless, making the perception of rejection, in many cases, completely nonexistent (Hallowell, 2021).

It is also essential to recognize that it is not easy for those on the other side. Having a partner with ADHD who may also suffer from RSD is challenging since we must deal with rapid changes and attempts in their moods. This rapid emotional fluctuation underscores the imperative need to distinguish between the genuine emotional responses of RSD and other mood-related conditions. This insight is essential to ensure that those struggling with RSD receive appropriate and specific treatment.

As knowledge of RSD grows, mental health practitioners can better spot signs in their patients and provide more tailored care. This advancement in our understanding of RSD enables the introduction of targeted therapy approaches that address the disease's emotional and neurological elements. The combination of treatment and medicine is positioned as a successful technique for relieving RSD symptoms.

Finally, recognizing RSD as a unique emotional difficulty allows individuals to understand and handle its complexity better. While people with ADHD have an innate ability to empathize, which enriches their relationships and develops strong connections, addressing RSD allows a more comprehensive and balanced view of emotional experiences throughout the ADHD range. In this process, the medical community and society may help to create a more understanding and supportive environment for persons affected with RSD.

Possible Disadvantages of Empathy

Our complexity as human beings is manifested in the diversity of emotions and personalities that each of us possesses, shaping our daily interactions. Empathy emerges as a distinctive ability in this fascinating emotional fabric that allows us to connect with others on a deeper level. However, like any powerful tool, empathy can have ramifications, depending on how it is channeled and perceived in different situations.

Empathy, when exercised in a balanced and positive way, can strengthen our relationships and foster deeper understanding between individuals. By understanding the emotions and perspectives of others, we create the foundation for solidarity, cooperation, and building genuine connections. Empathy acts as a bridge that unites people, allowing the construction of more authentic and enriching relationships.

However, empathy can also have its challenges when channeled excessively or negatively. In some cases, feeling the emotions of others intensely can lead to an overwhelming emotional burden. Those who are particularly empathetic may find themselves absorbed in the emotional experiences of others, leading to significant emotional burnout.

Additionally, excessive empathy can make establishing healthy boundaries in relationships difficult. The lack of distinction between one's emotions and those of others can result in an emotional fusion that impacts individual autonomy. Establishing clear boundaries becomes essential to preserving the emotional well-being of both yourself and others.

It is crucial to recognize that empathy, like any human skill, requires balance and discernment. The key lies in cultivating conscious empathy, where you can understand and share the emotions of others without losing sight of self-care and emotional autonomy.

The inherent complexities of ADHD, characterized by difficulties in attention, impulse control, and hyperactivity, often require consistent understanding and patience from partners. However, the cumulative impact of this emotional labor can lead to heightened stress and emotional fatigue.

Being a supportive partner to someone with ADHD involves navigating a dynamic landscape of emotions, behaviors, and daily challenges. Individuals in this role may find themselves constantly adapting to the ever-shifting needs and experiences of their partner with ADHD. The need for continuous understanding and support can take a toll on their emotional well-being, leading to emotional drain.

The emotional drain may stem from various sources, including the constant need to provide reassurance, understand the fluctuations in mood and attention, and adapt to the unpredictable nature of ADHD-related behaviors. Partners may also grapple with the frustration of witnessing their loved ones face hurdles in various aspects of life, from work to relationships, due to the challenges posed by ADHD.

Moreover, the emotional drain can manifest as a persistent worry about the well-being and success of the individual with ADHD. Partners may experience a heightened sense of responsibility, feeling compelled to ensure that their loved ones have the necessary support systems in place to cope with the daily challenges associated with the disorder. This heightened emotional investment can lead to chronic stress and emotional fatigue over time.

To address the emotional drain associated with supporting a partner with ADHD, individuals may benefit from establishing healthy boundaries, seeking support from friends, family, or support groups, and prioritizing self-care. Additionally, seeking professional guidance, such as therapy or counseling, can provide tools and strategies for managing the emotional toll and enhancing the overall well-being of both individuals in the relationship. Let's look at some potential disadvantages that misusing empathy with your partner can bring:

- **Frustration with persistent difficulties:** Although empathy can help understand the challenges of ADHD, persistent difficulties can lead to frustration. This is especially true if strategies and solutions don't seem to work, which can test patience and understanding.

- **Planning and organization challenges:** The impulsivity and attention problems associated with ADHD can affect the planning and organization of the relationship. Empathy can help understand these challenges but can also create tensions when more structure is required.

- **Unequal emotional load:** Unequal emotional load may arise in the relationship, as the person without ADHD may feel a responsibility to provide constant support. This can create emotional imbalances and affect the dynamics of the relationship.

- **Losing objectivity:** Emotional connection can hinder the ability to separate one's own emotions from those of others, which could lead to decisions based on empathy rather than more objective considerations. This challenge can especially arise in professional settings or important decisions that require a more detached and analytical approach.

Tool 2: Compassion

Compassion in a relationship, especially when one partner has attention deficit hyperactivity disorder, involves a profound ability to connect with the suffering and challenges that the partner with ADHD may experience. It goes beyond empathy, requiring genuine understanding and active commitment to alleviate difficulties and protect the relationship.

When your partner has ADHD, it is essential to feel compassion for the times when they face undeserved challenges due to the nature of their condition. This compassion is linked to emotional support and a willingness to take practical steps to help manage ADHD, such as establishing structured routines or finding strategies to improve communication.

Instead of feeling pity, compassion toward your partner with ADHD involves recognizing their worth and strengths while working together to address any difficulties that may arise. Compassion comes from actively listening to their experiences and appreciating their efforts to overcome the obstacles associated with ADHD.

The characteristics of a compassionate person in a relationship with someone who has ADHD include a heightened capacity for empathy and being easily moved by the challenges your partner faces. Compassion is evidenced by selfless and generous acts to alleviate the suffering or stresses associated with ADHD.

On the path taken by you for building and maintaining a healthy relationship with your partner who has attention deficit hyperactivity disorder, compassion plays a key role. In this deeper exploration, we'll offer helpful strategies for integrating compassion into your daily life with your partner, giving you tools to strengthen your connection and support ADHD management:

- **Celebrate progress:** Acknowledging and celebrating progress, no matter how small creates a positive atmosphere in the relationship. Whether overcoming daily challenges or completing seemingly impossible tasks, these shared victories reinforce the sense of teamwork. Establishing this ritual of celebration not only encourages positivity but also strengthens motivation to face the challenges ahead.

- **Be patient:** Patience in managing ADHD is a deliberate act of understanding. Recognize that the path to effective management is continuous and often involves a learning curve. Be patient with this process and give your partner the time and space to address their unique challenges. Patience reduces tensions and fosters an environment of support and mutual understanding.

- **Offer support:** Tangible support is a powerful expression of compassion. From helping with organization to offering gentle reminders, these acts demonstrate an active commitment to your partner's well-being.

Being a trusted and supportive presence can make a significant difference in times of struggle. Providing constant support creates an environment where the couple feels supported, making it easier to overcome ADHD-related obstacles.

Compassion in the Modern Era

Concern arises about the apparent decline of compassion in our social interactions in the contemporary era. This complex phenomenon can be attributed to a number of factors that have transformed the dynamics of our relationships and shaped the way we perceive and respond to the needs of others.

First, modern society's excessive individualism has led to an excessive valuing of personal success and self-sufficiency. In this context, attention to the concerns of others is often displaced, relegating compassion to the background.

The pervasive influence of technology constitutes another significant element in this equation. As digital interactions replace face-to-face communication, the empathy and compassion inherent in personal connections can fade, making room for colder, more distant interactions.

Furthermore, the accelerated pace of life characteristic of contemporary times contributes to more focused attention on the individual, with busy agendas and a constant search for personal goals. This frantic pursuit of goals can lead to a decreased sensitivity to the needs of others, thereby eroding the basis of compassion.

The inequalities and conflicts present in the contemporary world also play a crucial role. Economic, social, and political disparities generate exacerbated competition, undermining solidarity and fostering individualistic attitudes that distort the expression of compassion.

In some contexts, the lack of awareness and education about the importance of compassion and ethical values is also an influential factor. The absence of a moral foundation can contribute to losing these essential qualities in modern society.

Finally, media desensitization, marked by constant exposure to negative news and traumatic events, can decrease emotional sensitivity. This phenomenon triggers an anesthetized response to the suffering of others, undermining the basis of collective compassion.

Despite these challenges, it is imperative to recognize that numerous examples of compassion and solidarity persist in the contemporary world. Various people and organizations are working to counteract these trends and build more empathetic communities. Reflecting on these factors and promoting ethical awareness and education are essential steps toward revitalizing compassion in our modern society.

Tool 3: ADHD Empathetic Communication

As you communicate with adults with ADHD, you begin to notice that this disorder not only manifests itself in difficulties with concentration but also impacts organization, planning, and completion of tasks, as well as the ability to set priorities. These types of variations are essential in any stable and organized couple. If one of the two goes through these challenges, it can result in poor time management and, consequently, a diminished performance of all their potential.

Effective communication is the cornerstone for achieving success and fostering harmony in various aspects of life. It is an undeniable reality, and acknowledging this fact can significantly save us from wasting valuable time. Embracing the intrinsic importance of communication empowers individuals to recognize that the key to enhancing relationships lies within their grasp.

When we examine the profound impact of communication, we see that it has the potential to shape our interactions, resolve conflicts, and strengthen connections. This depends on accepting the responsibility that comes with effective communication. That's the only way we can open ourselves up to a world of opportunities to improve and enrich the ties we share with others.

This premise becomes even more relevant when ADHD is a factor in the equation. You cannot choose the most inherent aspects of the other when communicating, although you can go in search of the other, and they must also meet you halfway. On the other hand, they must be willing to communicate with you effectively.

The unique dynamics that ADHD presents require a thoughtful and strategic approach to building and maintaining a meaningful connection between partners. However, knowing that this strategy will also involve effort is key. You will need to see the "grays" in a world that sometimes seems black and white and appreciate the diversity instead of getting angry or frustrated. In short, you must recognize that not all of us communicate in the same way.

Recognizing diversity in communication styles becomes the first crucial step. Coping with ADHD involves discussing and defining preferences and incorporating strategies that meet the needs of both partners. Whether through a shared calendar, written reminders, or verbal cues, clarity in communication channels emerges as a cornerstone that allows couples to build a strong and understanding connection.

We are talking about cultivating an environment of communication where positive reinforcement becomes the central axis. This idea involves encouraging openness and honesty and expressing gratitude for the couple's communication efforts. This continuous practice of positive feedback strengthens the relationship and establishes a culture of mutual understanding and support.

Regular check-ins sustain constant communication, an intentional practice that allows both partners to share challenges, celebrate successes, and collaboratively address concerns. This proactive approach reinforces the fundamental idea that both voices are invaluable in the relationship, promoting a sense of equity and participation. Ultimately, this approach not only makes it easier to overcome obstacles but also enriches the relationship, transforming it into a shared journey toward growth and lasting connection.

Also, lack of attention can make the person less organized and consistent in their daily life. They can make seemingly simple mistakes but have significant consequences in personal, work, or academic areas.

For example, constant distraction and forgetfulness often include creating to-do lists or adopting highly structured habits to avoid overlooking essential matters. It can even be obsessive. In these cases, people incorporate behaviors that only add intensity and stress to people who already have enough of their own. Perfectionistic attitudes with excessive expectations are thought of as compensatory obsessive defenses (Lopez Gomez, 2024).

Dealing with these characteristics of ADHD can present additional challenges for a couple. The couple may find it necessary to understand and accept the quirks related to organization and care. Occasional mistakes and lost items may require patience and emotional support. Fostering an environment of mutual understanding where the partner with ADHD does not feel judged for their difficulties is essential.

To facilitate the concentration of couples with ADHD, it is crucial to provide a conducive environment, reducing external stimuli and providing quiet spaces. Accepting the need for moments of excitement to focus on specific projects and understanding the need for last-minute focus on task completion is also key. Instead of seeing these behaviors as obstacles, couples can learn to work together to find strategies and routines that allow for more harmonious and satisfying functioning in the relationship.

The Depth of Human Communication

Communication with others constitutes a fundamental aspect of the human experience, an interaction that goes beyond the simple transmission of information. At its core, communication is not limited to verbal expression but encompasses a full spectrum of expressions, including gestures, looks, tone of voice, and other forms of nonverbal communication. Let's look at the meaning of human communication and its relevance in building meaningful relationships and cohesive societies.

Communication, in its most basic form, involves the transmission of thoughts, emotions, and information between individuals. However, its scope goes beyond mere data transfer. It stands as the foundation on which human connections are built. Communicative interaction informs and establishes emotional bonds, fosters mutual understanding, and nourishes the social fabric that sustains our communities.

In today's digital age, where virtual interactions are often prevalent, it is crucial to reflect on the authenticity of communication. Effective communication conveys information, builds connections, fosters understanding, and strengthens relationships. Beyond instant messages and social media, accurate communication involves the ability to understand and be understood, to recognize underlying emotions, and to build bridges of empathy between individuals. It is a dynamic process that requires active listening, attention to nonverbal cues, and a willingness to share openly and honestly.

Effective communication extends to a societal level. A well-communicated society is one in which ideas flow, differences are resolved through dialogue, and diversity is appreciated as a wealth that strengthens the social fabric. The absence of meaningful communication can lead to misunderstandings, conflicts, and loss of human connection, leading to social fragmentation and mistrust.

Chapter Four

Learn To Regulate Your Emotions

Most do not understand that when a person is faced with a task in which he has strong and immediate personal interest, either because he really enjoys it or because he fears that not doing the task will quickly bring some very unpleasant consequence, the chemistry of the brain is instantly altered to mobilize. And most don't know that this alteration of brain chemistry is not under voluntary control. ADHD clearly appears to be a problem of willpower failure, but it is actually a problem with the interacting dynamics of emotion, working memory, and the chemistry of the brain.

–Dr. Thomas Brown

Within ADHD's complex landscape, the ability to regulate emotions emerges as a linchpin for building and maintaining healthy connections. This chapter delves into the profound importance of mastering emotional regulation in ADHD relationships, highlighting the profound impact of emotional intensity and offering practical strategies for cultivating more resilient and fulfilling bonds.

Individuals with ADHD frequently encounter heightened emotional responses, ranging from intense joy to frustration or impatience. These emotional fluctuations significantly shape interactions, influencing the overall emotional tone of relationships. Recognizing and acknowledging the role of emotional intensity is the initial stride toward fostering an environment conducive to robust and positive connections.

Uncontrolled emotions within the realm of ADHD relationships can instigate misunderstandings, conflicts, and heightened stress levels. Partners may find it challenging to comprehend the unpredictable emotional shifts, potentially leading to frustration and tension. Effectively addressing this dynamic necessitates a collective commitment to understanding and managing the emotional aspects inherent in ADHD.

Emotional regulation, a cornerstone in navigating relationships affected by ADHD, demands the development of practical emotion management skills. It transcends mere self-control, entailing self-awareness, identifying triggers, and implementing coping mechanisms tailored to address emotional challenges.

This chapter will illuminate three fundamental pillars for promoting emotional regulation in ADHD relationships. These pillars encompass the vital elements of self-awareness, open communication, and coping mechanisms, all essential tools for constructing resilient and thriving relationships amidst the unique emotional landscape intensified by ADHD.

Furthermore, beyond merely managing intense emotions, the chapter emphasizes the cultivation of emotional resilience. This resilience involves deriving lessons from experiences, adapting to challenges, and fostering a positive emotional climate within the relationship. Doing so establishes a protective layer, enhancing the overall durability and quality of the emotional connection.

Practical Tips for Emotional Regulation in ADHD Relationships

- **Daily check-ins:** Establish a routine of daily check-ins with your partner to discuss emotional states and potential triggers. This fosters awareness and enables proactive support.

- **Mindfulness practices:** Incorporate mindfulness techniques, such as deep breathing or meditation, into your daily routine. These practices enhance self-awareness and contribute to emotional stability.

- **Shared emotional tool kit:** Collaborate with your partner to create a tool kit of coping mechanisms that work for both of you. Having a shared resource fosters mutual understanding and reinforces emotional support.

Tool 4: Emotional Management

ADHD is not a disability; it's a different ability.

–Edward M. Hallowell

ADHD, a chronic disorder that affects both children and adults, directly affects the management and perception of emotions. Focusing primarily on childhood, a crucial period for learning to regulate and express emotions, we observe that, although the feelings in children with ADHD do not differ from those of their peers, the difficulty in controlling them and their prolonged intensity can hinder their daily lives.

Due to problems in emotional self-regulation, people with ADHD are often misinterpreted as "too intense" or, conversely, as indifferent. These people may react disproportionately to small adversities, experience a hot temper and difficulty calming down, or worry excessively about seemingly trivial matters. As they grow, they learn to manage their emotions, although at a different pace and sometimes with the need for specialized assistance.

In relationships where one partner struggles with attention deficit hyperactivity disorder, the landscape of emotional dynamics can be intricate and challenging. Understanding and effectively managing emotions becomes essential to fostering a resilient and harmonious connection. This exploration delves into the complexities of emotional management in the context of relationships affected by ADHD, shedding light on the feasibility of controlling emotions and the unique emotional perception that couples experience.

The question of whether emotions can be managed effectively occupies a central place in the field of relationships affected by ADHD. Managing emotions involves recognizing and regulating one's emotional responses and understanding how these emotions impact the dynamics of the relationship. It is a nuanced process that requires self-awareness, communication, and collaborative efforts to create an environment conducive to emotional well-being.

Effectively managing emotions requires a multifaceted approach. Partners must navigate the ebbs and flows of emotional intensity that often accompany ADHD. Strategies such as mindfulness, open communication, and shared coping mechanisms become essential tools in the emotional management tool kit. The journey does not involve erasing emotions but understanding them, expressing them, and channeling them in constructive ways that improve the relationship's overall health.

Understanding how a partner with ADHD perceives and experiences emotions is essential to fostering empathy and support. ADHD can manifest in unique emotional patterns, often characterized by increased intensity and rapid fluctuations. The couple may deal with frustration, impulsivity, and difficulties maintaining emotional coherence.

This section delves into the emotional panorama from the perspective of the individual with ADHD. Let's explore the disorder's impact on emotional perception, shedding light on how external factors, stressors, and daily interactions can amplify emotional responses. Acknowledging and validating these emotional experiences is a crucial step toward building a connection of support and understanding.

The Importance Behind Emotional Management

Emotional management skills play a critical role in personal and professional growth, contributing to the broader framework of emotional intelligence. These skills involve regulating and navigating emotional responses effectively for personal well-being and fostering positive interactions in the professional setting. It is necessary to recognize the importance of emotional management skills, highlighting key components such as reflection, acceptance, perspective, and empathy (Indeed, 2021).

Emotional management skills are paramount for professionals as they help them maintain composure and make rational decisions, especially in high-stress scenarios. Cultivating these skills can help people improve their leadership capabilities and become more effective team members and leaders in various industries.

These people also incorporate reflection as a fundamental emotional management skill. Being reflective facilitates a large part of the path to growing as a person and also in the art of understanding your partner with ADHD. Reflection allows you to delve deeper into the root causes of your emotional reactions. For example, in a workplace conflict, taking time to reflect can help separate personal emotions from the situation. This reflective process facilitates conflict resolution by allowing people to identify whether their disagreement arises from the decision itself or personal insecurities related to the circumstances (Indeed, 2021).

Acceptance is another crucial aspect of emotional management skills, emphasizing the importance of acknowledging one's emotions without judgment. This ability allows people to respond rationally to challenging situations, promoting faster recovery from emotional reactions and allowing for a sharper focus on the tasks at hand. Additionally, learning to accept one's emotions fosters empathy toward others, as individuals can draw parallels between their experiences and those of their colleagues.

Developing a sense of perspective is essential to managing emotions effectively. For example, recognizing that nervousness before a presentation is a common experience among successful professionals puts those emotions into perspective. This understanding reinforces that emotions are natural reactions that can be overcome, allowing people to carry out their tasks confidently. Cultivating emotional management skills is essential for personal and professional success.

Of course, we also have empathy. Empathy may be the cornerstone of emotional management. The skill connects you with others deeper by allowing you to understand and relate to their feelings. Integrating empathy into the workplace fosters meaningful relationships, prevents conflict, and improves collaboration. Acknowledging a colleague's struggles and frustrations allows people to offer support and collaborate on practical solutions, creating a positive and productive work environment.

The emotional intensity associated with ADHD can contribute to the development of disorders such as anxiety or depression. The resulting behaviors often lead to rejection in social settings, especially at school, where lack of understanding may be more pronounced. This scenario creates a vicious circle: Social rejection leads to isolation, generating self-esteem problems and a negative perception of themselves.

Breaking this cycle through understanding and support at school and home is essential. Understanding the behaviors of people with ADHD and helping them identify and regulate their emotions becomes crucial to facilitating their integration into the socio-emotional world. Appropriate pedagogy and support can play a fundamental role in developing emotional skills and building positive self-esteem in those facing the challenge of ADHD.

Here, we embark on a journey that requires patience, communication, and a willingness to accept the uniqueness of emotional experiences within this context. Through this exploration, we seek to understand the challenges and discover pathways to cultivate emotional resilience and strengthen the emotional bonds that define these relationships.

Tool 5: Become Self-Aware

Moving forward in a relationship is never easy. It involves work, will, and effort on both sides of the equation and always has an associated cost. When ADHD enters the picture, all that effort to keep a loving relationship afloat, strengthen it, and carry it into the future requires a nuanced approach. Self-awareness emerges as a powerful tool in this intricate journey of love.

ADHD presents unique challenges to romantic relationships, influencing communication, emotional expression, and overall connection. Before delving into the realm of self-awareness, it is essential to understand the specific ways ADHD can manifest in the context of love. Recognizing the potential impact of ADHD provides a foundation for developing self-awareness to address these challenges.

Self-awareness involves an honest and reflective examination of one's strengths and challenges. For people with ADHD, this means recognizing the positive attributes that contribute to the relationship and the aspects that may pose difficulties. Accepting personal strengths and challenges allows for a more authentic and transparent connection with a romantic partner.

ADHD often comes with triggers that can influence emotional responses and behaviors. Becoming self-aware involves identifying these triggers and recognizing behavioral patterns that may arise in a romantic relationship.

Effective communication is the cornerstone of any successful relationship. For people with ADHD, it is essential to become self-aware in this area. This includes recognizing how ADHD can affect the expression of emotions and understanding personal communication styles. Developing self-awareness in communication fosters a more precise understanding between partners and facilitates a more harmonious connection.

Ultimately, cultivating self-awareness in romantic relationships affected by ADHD is a transformative journey. It allows people to face challenges gracefully, fostering resilience and deepening connection with their partners. Let's explore the importance of cultivating self-awareness as a transformative tool to improve the dynamics of romantic relationships affected by ADHD.

Individuals grappling with ADHD can discover practical strategies aimed at enhancing self-awareness in the context of their romantic relationships. From mindfulness techniques to insightful journaling exercises, these tools serve as invaluable resources for delving deeper into one's psyche and understanding the dynamics at play with their partners. The cultivation of self-awareness emerges as a vital instrument for fostering mutual understanding, effective communication, and heightened empathy.

A Journey to the Inner Self

Throughout history, philosophers, psychologists, and scientists have been fascinated by the question of when and how humans become self-aware. Although there is no absolute consensus on the exact age at which this occurs, evidence suggests that self-awareness emerges gradually during human development.

Babies exhibit signs of awareness of themselves and their environment from the earliest stages of life. The ability to recognize yourself in a mirror, known as the mirror test, is a significant milestone in developing self-awareness. This test involves observing whether an individual can recognize their own image in a mirror. Although most babies do not pass this test before 18 months, it suggests that self-awareness is linked to cognitive and social development.

Self-awareness is not a static phenomenon; it evolves throughout life. Children develop a deeper understanding of themselves, their identity, and their emotions during childhood. Language acquisition is crucial, allowing children to express and reflect on their inner thoughts. As children grow, so does their awareness of themselves about others and the world around them.

Adolescence marks another critical phase in the development of self-awareness. Hormonal changes, social experiences, and reflections on personal identity lead adolescents to question who they are and how they fit into the world. This period is often characterized by the search for independence and identity formation, which drives individuals to explore and define their values, beliefs, and goals.

Neuroscience has also shed light on the biological substrates of self-awareness. Neuroimaging studies have identified brain regions, such as the prefrontal cortex, that play a key role in self-reflection and self-awareness. The maturity of these brain areas, which continues into early adulthood, is associated with a more significant development of self-awareness.

Introspection and self-reflection, fundamental practices in developing self-awareness, can be cultivated throughout life, leading to greater self-awareness in adulthood. However, self-awareness does not reach its fullness in adolescence. It continues to evolve throughout life. Experiences, challenges, and personal growth contribute to a deeper understanding of oneself.

Collaborative Identification of Triggers

When we look at couples with ADHD, we soon understand that collaboration stands out as a cornerstone in identifying triggers and patterns associated with the challenges that may arise. We talk about both actively participating in this process—together—in society. Thus, we proactively manage potential problems and foster an environment of understanding and support.

Regular discussions focused on identifying triggers serve as a proactive strategy to strengthen emotional bonds within the relationship. By jointly recognizing and understanding these triggers, couples can develop strategies to deal with them more effectively. This collaborative approach encourages partners to explore and acknowledge specific situations or stimuli that may trigger ADHD-related challenges.

This collaborative identification not only enhances problem-solving skills but also contributes to a shared consciousness that shapes the trajectory of the relationship, promoting resilience and unity in the face of challenges.

Routine and Emotional Climate Records

Establishing routine check-ins provides a structured framework for partners to intentionally and consistently address their relationship's emotional climate. These scheduled sessions are dedicated to open and constructive dialogue, offering opportunities to express feelings, address concerns, and celebrate achievements together. Intentional engagement with these controls is a powerful catalyst, fostering deeper mutual understanding and strengthening emotional intimacy.

During these check-ins, partners can reflect on recent experiences, both positive and challenging, and collaboratively identify patterns in emotional responses. This shared documentation becomes a resource for meeting future challenges, allowing partners to build on past successes and lessons learned.

Constant communication within this structured framework helps build a foundation of trust and emotional security. It encourages partners to actively participate in each other's emotional worlds, fostering a supportive environment where both individuals feel heard and understood. As a result, routine check-ins become more than just a scheduled activity: they become a vital practice that contributes to the ongoing health and resilience of the relationship.

Cultivate Patience

Developing self-awareness is an ongoing process that requires patience and understanding. Partners must approach this journey with a mindset of continuous growth, celebrating progress, and learning from challenges together. Cultivating patience fosters an environment where self-awareness can flourish organically.

Patience, viewed through the lens of emotional intelligence, entails being aware of our strengths and weaknesses. Recognizing that we are not perfect and that perfection is not necessary is essential in cultivating patience with oneself. Our virtues and imperfections are crucial in shaping our identity and achieving emotional balance in life.

These practical strategies serve as pillars, fostering an environment where partners can deepen their understanding, strengthen their connection, and face the unique challenges that ADHD poses with resilience and grace. The journey of fostering self-awareness in romantic relationships affected by ADHD is a multifaceted endeavor that requires dedication and a spirit of collaboration.

Fostering patience with oneself involves addressing the self-demand often imposed on areas believed to be controllable. This attitude can be detrimental, leading to an emotionally imbalanced life. It is crucial to understand that there are aspects beyond our control and to accept this reality to avoid unnecessary disappointments. Lacking patience with oneself can result in an exhausting, chaotic existence with significant emotional costs.

ADHD Self-Awareness

Most people with ADHD have always been aware of their uniqueness. Parents, teachers, employers, partners, and friends have told them that they don't fit the conventional mold and that they need to work harder to achieve something meaningful in life.

Like immigrants, they were urged to assimilate into the predominant culture and adopt conventional behaviors. However, they did not receive the necessary guidance on how to achieve this. They have not communicated the essential revelation that no matter how hard they tried to adjust, they could not achieve it. They faced failures, compounded by accusations of lack of effort or dedication, since ADHD in adults carries the stigma of not applying yourself as necessary (Dodson, 2023).

It is peculiar to call a "disorder" something that has numerous positive characteristics. Those with an ADHD-type nervous system excel at problem-solving, confronting situations that have stumped others, and finding solutions. They are friendly, nice people with a sense of humor. They exhibit what Paul Wender calls "relentless determination," approaching challenges in various ways until they master them, although they lose interest when they no longer present a challenge.

If I had to list the qualities that ensure success, I would highlight intelligence, its creative use, popularity, persistence, and willingness to help. I would value possessing many of the characteristic traits of those with ADHD.

The main challenge in understanding and addressing ADHD has been the implicit and incorrect assumption that those who experience it could and should conform to the standard of others. For both neurotypical people and adults with ADHD, this is a detailed portrait of why those with attention deficit act the way they do (Dodson, 2023).

Tool 6: It's All About Regulation

The unique emotional challenges present in relationships with ADHD require a specialized approach to addressing them. This tool stands out as a fundamental pillar in this set of strategies, emphasizing the importance of implementing regulatory tactics to manage the inherent emotional fluctuations in these relationships effectively.

Individuals with ADHD naturally face difficulties in emotional regulation, evidenced by impulsive behaviors, sudden mood swings, and complicated management of frustration. In the context of relationships, these challenges not only impact the individual with ADHD but also influence the overall dynamics of the partnership, leading to misunderstandings, disruptions in communication, and an amplification of emotional tensions.

When emotional dysregulation is mentioned, it refers to a person's inability to manage their emotional responses adequately. In this state, emotions tend to flow more quickly and deeply, increasing the likelihood of intensely expressing those feelings in public settings. This often leads to a subsequent sense of guilt or shame.

In the context of ADHD, emotional dysregulation often manifests itself through behavioral patterns, with impulsivity being an obvious sign. Although indicators such as impulsivity are easily identifiable, there are other more subtle ones, such as lower resilience, the inability to regain emotional balance, a deep immersion in conflict, or the persistence of negative emotions.

These patterns of emotional dysregulation can significantly impact personal relationships with individuals who have ADHD. The intense expression of emotions and challenges to restore emotional balance can create tensions in communication and make conflict resolution difficult. It is crucial to recognize and understand these aspects to promote a more understanding and supportive dynamic in relationships with people experiencing emotional dysregulation due to ADHD.

Reflecting on emotional regulation becomes essential in this context, as it involves recognizing and understanding the inherent difficulties in managing emotions for both the person with ADHD and their partner. Awareness of these challenges provides the foundation for implementing strategies that foster an emotionally healthy environment, promoting mutual understanding and stability in the relationship.

The Regulatory Tool Kit

- **Structured routines:** Establishing structured routines provides a sense of predictability, alleviating the anxiety and emotional volatility associated with ADHD. Consistency in daily activities contributes to emotional regulation, fostering a stable relationship environment.

- **Setting limits:** Clearly defined boundaries are crucial in managing emotional challenges. Establishing acceptable behavior and communicating expectations helps prevent misunderstandings and minimizes emotional turmoil within the relationship.

- **Educational resources:** Increasing understanding of ADHD through educational resources benefits both partners. Knowledge about the disorder fosters empathy and equips people with practical strategies to support their partners in their emotional struggles.

- **Therapeutic support:** Seeking professional help through couples therapy or individual counseling is a proactive step. Mental health professionals offer guidance, teach coping mechanisms, and provide a neutral space to discuss emotional challenges within the relationship.

- **Strategic planning:** Developing strategies to anticipate and manage possible emotional triggers becomes essential. Proactively addressing situations that can provoke intense emotions allows people with ADHD and their partners to deal with challenges more effectively.

Real Stories

My message for everyone is the same: that if we can learn to identify, express, and harness our feelings, even the most challenging ones, we can use those emotions to help us create positive, satisfying lives.

–Marc Brackett

From an early age, I was always a passionate and emotional person. My feelings seemed to have a life of their own, guiding me through moments of unbridled joy or deep valleys of sadness. Part of me probably wanted to regularize the situation, but I couldn't. Those comings and goings, those sudden jumps in energy and mood, those resounding falls, added adrenaline to everyday life. However, meditation, reflection, and restraint taught me something important.

As I grew older, I realized I needed to learn to manage these emotions to live a more balanced and healthy life. My turning point occurred during college when I faced a series of academic and personal challenges. At this moment, I decided to spend time introspecting and learning to regulate my emotions. I understood that "He who got angry, lost." I understood in college the power behind strategic thinking and began to regulate my emotions.

I'm not talking about canceling or ignoring them—quite the opposite. Regulating your emotions means that you know them like the back of your hand. You have the necessary information and the ability to "turn the volume down a bit" when necessary. So, I embarked on a journey of self-discovery, using meditation and writing as tools to understand my emotional reactions better. I developed skills to reflect on my emotions, accept them without judging myself, and put them in perspective. This personal evolution not only improved my overall well-being but also became a valuable asset when I entered a relationship with my partner, who has ADHD.

This teaching profoundly transformed my personal relationships. My partner experienced intense emotions and often expressed frustration at not being able to control them. I was able to offer compassionate support and help my partner identify and understand his own emotions.

I learned to be patient and understanding during moments of distraction, understanding that they were part of my partner's journey with ADHD. My journey of learning about emotional regulation has not only improved my quality of life but has also strengthened my relationship with my partner with ADHD.

Chapter Five

Non-ADHD Partners: Support and Understanding

The thing about ADHD is that it's actually great. I love the way my brain works. I'm funny and flexible and creative and adventurous. My frustrations mostly stem from trying to force my ADHD brain to function in a non-ADHD world.

–Brittney Bush Bollay

In this chapter, we will delve into the essential role of non-ADHD couples and highlight their valuable contributions to fostering a healthy, thriving connection. The primary goal is to provide knowledge, understanding, and practical strategies to empower non-ADHD couples to support their loved ones effectively.

The purpose is to offer non-ADHD couples a comprehensive understanding of the challenges their counterparts may face and provide practical tools to address these challenges together. I invite you to explore the dynamics of relationships affected by ADHD as we seek to foster empathy, communication, and resilience within the couple. Additionally, we high-light the crucial role of the non-ADHD couple in creating a supportive en-vironment that promotes the strengths and potential of both individuals.

We will also explore various strategies designed to improve the non-ADHD partner's ability to support and understand their loved one with ADHD. These strategies encompass effective communication tech-niques, collaborative problem-solving approaches, and empathy develop-ment. We will delve into the importance of self-care for the partner with-out ADHD, recognizing their unique challenges and providing tools to overcome them, maintaining a healthy balance in the relationship.

Understanding and supporting a partner with ADHD can be reward-ing, but it is not without challenges. Partners without ADHD may face issues such as managing impulsivity, dealing with difficulties related to attention, and coping with the emotional dynamics that ADHD can in-troduce into the relationship.

Through knowledge, empathy, and active participation, non-ADHD partners can be crucial in building a thriving, supportive partnership for both people involved.

Problems resulting from ADHD can color relationships with a series of complex challenges. Experiencing this dynamic carries an additional bur-den when only one of the members of the couple faces ADHD, generating complex feelings and situations that are difficult to manage.

The crisis in our marriage led us to seek professional help and education about ADHD. Through this process, we better understood how ADHD affected our dynamics. It wasn't simply disinterest or lack of commitment but a genuine challenge that required a collaborative approach. We saw positive changes as we learned to identify and address these challenges together.

Facing the relationship issues associated with ADHD not only strengthened our connection but also allowed us to grow individually. We learned to communicate more effectively, set realistic expectations, and appreciate the unique strengths each brings to the relationship. With love, patience, and understanding, we overcame the initial tensions.

Reflecting on this experience, I can say with certainty that couples can be significantly strengthened by addressing the challenges of ADHD positively and collaboratively. Mutual understanding and love can become a solid foundation to overcome any obstacle, allowing the relationship to evolve into a space of mutual understanding and support.

In the journey of love with ADHD, these tools become the foundations that strengthen the bond, transforming challenges into opportunities for more profound, more resilient love.

Tool 7: Facing Challenging Times

When facing difficult times in a relationship affected by ADHD, collaboration becomes an essential tool to address challenges effectively. Communication not only becomes paramount but also takes on even greater importance. Establishing a safe space for open dialogue becomes the cornerstone of facing these critical moments. Instead of viewing challenges as insurmountable obstacles, couples can embrace them as opportunities to strengthen their connection and better understand the complexities of ADHD in relational dynamics.

Additionally, providing practical advice to address these challenges can include specific communication strategies, such as using clear and compassionate language, avoiding blame, and focusing on constructive solutions.

As a couple thrives on shared happy moments and builds beautiful memories and lessons learned through them, difficult times test our relationships. Challenging moments demand more from us and invite us to rethink everything we are doing. That's what it's all about: embracing the challenge.

Encouraging partners to view challenges as opportunities for mutual learning can also strengthen the resilience of the relationship. A collaborative approach under challenging times creates fertile ground for mutual understanding and helps build a solid foundation for a long-lasting relationship.

That is why we repeatedly highlight the transformative capacity of reflection when relating to your partner. Recognizing the value of sharing specific moments of past challenges in the relationship affected by ADHD and how jointly addressing them contributed to strengthening the bond. Part of growing as a couple means looking back and celebrating the progress you've made. Remembering how to confront these challenges as a team solves immediate problems and lays the foundation for growing together and greater mutual understanding.

It is essential to emphasize that facing difficult times as a team involves overcoming immediate obstacles and can deepen the connection between partners. The emphasis on a shared commitment to finding solutions also creates a fertile ground for joint problem-solving, where both partners feel equally invested in the relationship's well-being. These challenging moments become opportunities to learn and grow together, building resilience in the relationship.

Overcommitment and ADHD

Overcommitment is a common challenge faced by people with attention deficit hyperactivity disorder. It manifests itself in various aspects of your personal and professional life. It sheds light on the intricate interaction of neurological traits, social expectations, and the psychological dynamics of your partner with ADHD.

A prominent factor contributing to overcommitment in people with ADHD is what is known as "time blindness." Characterized by a distorted sense of time, people with ADHD often have difficulty accurately assessing the hands-on time needed to complete tasks. This neurologically predisposed misinterpretation can lead to taking on more responsibilities than can realistically be handled, resulting in unfinished tasks and additional stress. The paradox lies in the counterintuitive nature of creating further work without the time needed to complete it.

Another critical factor that drives over-engagement is the tendency of people with ADHD to engage in people-pleasing behaviors. Rooted in the rejection-sensitive dysphoria we saw earlier, this condition in which people fear rejection and work excessively to prove themselves indispensable, people with ADHD may willingly take on the burdens of others despite being overwhelmed by their feelings. This coping mechanism, often subconscious, creates a vicious cycle in which the individual's efforts to go above and beyond can lead to disappointment and, paradoxically, rejection.

Gender roles can exacerbate overcommitment, especially for women with ADHD. Societal expectations place a heavy burden on women to manage their own responsibilities and those of their children and spouses. Despite the unlikelihood of meeting these expectations due to their neurological condition, the fear of disappointing loved ones compels individuals with ADHD to take on all the responsibilities of modern femininity, perpetuating the cycle of over-commitment.

Fear of missing out (FOMO) has a considerable influence in shaping the tendency to overcommit among people with ADHD. On a personal level, anxiety about missing out on potential opportunities or being excluded from enjoyable activities can lead them to take on more responsibilities than they can handle. The powerful motivator behind this behavior is the desire to stay connected, keep up with others, and avoid the discomfort of feeling abandoned.

For people with ADHD, FOMO can manifest as a compelling force that intensifies the already present challenge of managing time and commitments. Fear of being left out or not being a part of exciting experiences can lead to a greater susceptibility to over-commitment. This inclination to overexert yourself to stay socially connected and engaged often arises from a genuine longing for inclusion and a sense of belonging.

Understanding the impact of FOMO on overcommitment is crucial to providing support and developing coping strategies for people with ADHD. It involves recognizing that the fear of missing out, when not managed effectively, can significantly contribute to stress and overwhelm. Helping people with ADHD navigate their social and professional lives by addressing these underlying concerns can contribute to a more balanced and sustainable approach to commitments.

This book seeks to understand the multifaceted nature of overcommitment in ADHD. People can work to develop effective coping strategies, encourage open communication, and set realistic limits. This comprehensive approach can pave the way to a more balanced and sustainable lifestyle, promoting personal and professional well-being and success.

Tool 8: Understanding Through Love

Understanding through love involves recognizing that, even if we do not suffer from ADHD, it is essential to highlight the transformative power of love when facing the complexities that our partner experiences in their relationship with us. Taking on this challenge involves not only accepting the particularities associated with ADHD but also unconditionally supporting our partner in the face of future challenges. It is a deep commit-ment to be present and supportive, recognizing that love is a feeling and a constant action that drives mutual understanding.

Incorporating concrete practices to express love and empathy becomes crucial. From small daily gestures to words of encouragement, these ac-tions can open gaps in our partner's understanding, showing that we are willing to adapt and grow together. Effective communication, focused on empathy, becomes an invaluable tool, allowing our words and actions to reflect our unconditional love.

Additionally, exploring new ways to express love and gratitude can fur-ther strengthen the emotional connection. From surprise gestures to reg-ularly expressing appreciation for our partner's efforts, these actions foster a positive and supportive environment. By reinforcing the importance of love as a force that transcends adversity, we are paving the way for a more enriching and meaningful relationship where mutual understanding flourishes and union is strengthened.

Practical tips to strengthen the relationship include the regular expres-sion of affection, which goes beyond words and translates into concrete gestures that demonstrate love and affection. From spontaneous hugs to small daily displays of affection, these actions create an environment of emotional security that contributes to the well-being of both partners.

Accepting each person's unique qualities in the relationship translates into cultivating the diversity and richness each person offers. Instead of seeing differences as obstacles, they can be celebrated as enriching elements that strengthen connection. This mutual acceptance creates an environ-ment of respect and understanding, allowing the relationship to grow in a healthy way.

Reinforcing the idea that a foundation of love promotes a positive at-mosphere highlights the importance of maintaining a constructive attitude even in difficult times. Love acts as a balm that relieves tension and fosters emotional intimacy.

Next, let's look at five examples of spontaneous and practical love that you can have with your partner who has ADHD:

- **Daily supportive gestures:** Instead of focusing solely on everyday tasks, I incorporated small, supportive gestures that my partner with ADHD would find meaningful. Preparing an encouraging note in the morning or leaving an organized list of the day's activities has proven an effective way to provide support without adding pressure. This simple gesture shows my understanding of daily challenges and provides constant encouragement.

- **Spaces of understanding:** Recognizing and respecting my partner's need for moments of tranquility and concentration is a tangible expression of love. Instead of interpreting these moments as distancing, I've learned to create spaces where they can immerse themselves in their interests and projects without unnecessary interruptions. This show of understanding reinforces the idea that I value their unique qualities and am willing to adapt to support their well-being.

- **Personalized adventures:** To incorporate fun and adventure into our relationship, I created "Custom Adventure Days." These special days are designed to tap into the passions and curiosities of my partner with ADHD. For example, if I find out that they've expressed an interest in astronomy, I can plan an evening of stargazing, complete with cozy blankets and a list of space trivia. These personalized adventures demonstrate my commitment to understanding and supporting their unique interests and provide us with shared moments full of excitement and connection.

- **Mindful Breaks and Stress Relief:** Recognizing the impact of stress on my partner's well-being, I've introduced mindful breaks into our routine. These breaks can include short meditation sessions, calming walks, or engaging in a shared hobby. By proactively integrating moments of relaxation, I aim to provide my partner with the tools to manage stress and maintain balance. This practical expression of love emphasizes my commitment to their mental and emotional health, fostering a supportive atmosphere within our relationship.

- **Joint Goal Setting and Celebrations:** To harness the power of collaboration, we engage in joint goal-setting sessions where we outline both individual and shared aspirations. Breaking down larger goals into manageable steps, we celebrate each achievement. This approach supports my partner's journey and reinforces a sense of accomplishment and shared progress within our relationship. By actively participating in their aspirations, I demonstrate my commitment to their growth and success, fostering a sense of teamwork and shared accomplishment.

Tool 9: Take Care of Yourself, Too

Maintaining individual well-being emerges as a fundamental pillar in building healthy relationships, where self-care becomes an essential practice. Recognizing and prioritizing self-care is not about selfishness but a necessary act so that both members of the couple can offer their best to the relationship. This self-care approach nurtures individual well-being and lays the foundation for a stronger, healthier connection between you.

Focusing on self-care involves recognizing individual needs and dedicating time and effort to meeting them. From managing stress to finding activities that provide pleasure and rest, this personal commitment translates into a greater ability to face relationship challenges with resilience. Understanding that self-care is not a luxury but necessary fosters an environment where individuals can grow and flourish independently.

Self-care benefits the individual and contributes significantly to the relationship's overall health. This self-love creates a positive domino effect, generating a dynamic in which both partners are emotionally equipped to offer mutual support. Ultimately, self-care becomes a catalyst for relationship flourishing, where individual strengths harmoniously merge to build a lasting and nurturing connection.

- **Establish healthy routines:** Creating daily and weekly routines provides structure and stability, essential elements in a relationship affected by ADHD. Establishing regular times for meals, rest, and quality time together allows both partners to anticipate and manage daily activities more effectively. Additionally, these routines provide a sense of predictability, which can help reduce the stress and anxiety associated with ADHD.

- **Maintain open communication about individual needs:** Encouraging open and honest communication about individual needs is crucial. Both partners must feel comfortable expressing what they require for their well-being. This may include quiet times for the partner with ADHD and periods of active support for the other. Setting clear expectations and understanding each other's needs contributes to an environment of mutual understanding and support.

- **Make time for personal interests:** Regularly dedicating time to personal interests is essential for self-care in a relationship with ADHD. Both partners should be free to pursue their passions through hobbies, physical activities, or personal projects. This space for individual growth strengthens self-esteem and enriches the relationship by allowing both to evolve independently.

- **Exercise regularly:** Regular physical exercise benefits mental and physical health. For those with ADHD, exercise can help release pent-up energy and improve concentration. Jointly committing to physical activities, such as walking together or participating in sports, promotes individual health and strengthens connection through shared experiences.

- **Plan time for rest:** Recognizing the importance of rest is crucial in self-care. Planning moments to disconnect and rest, whether through short naps, meditation, or simply enjoying quiet moments together, contributes to stress management and improves emotional well-being. This proactive approach to rest allows both partners to recharge and face daily challenges with greater mental and emotional clarity.

Tool 10: Go the Extra Mile!

Going the extra mile involves conscious actions and cultivating a proactive and ongoing commitment to nurturing and strengthening the relationship. I remember when I decided to surprise my partner by organizing an intimate dinner with his favorite dishes. This gesture required planning and effort but generated a deeper connection and meaningful shared moments. This additional act of caring demonstrated a willingness to go above and beyond to create special memories.

Surprise gestures of kindness have been powerful tools in my relationship. From small notes of encouragement to unexpected gifts that reflect the attention paid to my partner's wants and needs, these additional acts have helped strengthen the emotional bond. It's a way to show your partner you actively participate in each other's interests, strengthening our bond.

However, it's important to know that if you're going to get more involved, you need to do it genuinely. Taking an interest in the activities your partner is passionate about, even if not your main interest, opens a space for mutual understanding and reinforces the idea that the relationship is an ever-evolving collaboration. This strengthens the willingness to understand and support each other and face challenges together; learning about individual complexities and being there during difficult times have been additional efforts that have strengthened our connection.

Reflecting on this, it becomes clear that going the extra mile is a continuous and dynamic process. It is not an isolated act but a mindset of constant commitment that drives the relationship's growth. Communicating this dedication to continued growth reinforces the current connection and lays the foundation for a relationship that flourishes through mutual effort and consideration.

Going the extra mile means meeting basic expectations and embarking on a proactive and ongoing commitment to enrich connection and mutual support. In this context, we will explore three fundamental strategies that go beyond the conventional and aim to strengthen the relationship with your partner who faces the challenge of ADHD. From proactive organizing to actively engaging in specific coping strategies and creating a supportive environment, these strategies seek to not only understand the complexities of ADHD but also build a solid foundation for a long-lasting and nurturing relationship.

• Creating a Reflective Space in the Relationship

Building a supportive foundation in a relationship with a partner managing ADHD involves more than just sharing responsibilities; it requires a profound understanding and proactive approach. One effective way to demonstrate this is by envisioning and creating a reflective space accommodating your partner's concentration needs. This goes beyond a mere acknowledgment of ADHD; it reflects a genuine commitment to fostering an environment conducive to focus and success.

To implement this, consider preparing a quiet workspace tailored to your partner's preferences. Minimizing potential interruptions and distractions can significantly enhance their ability to concentrate. This effort communicates your awareness of their challenges and highlights your dedication to their comfort and overall success.

• Engaging in ADHD Coping Strategies

Going a step further in supporting a partner with ADHD involves active engagement in personalized coping strategies. This signifies a commitment to collaborative problem-solving and addressing the unique challenges posed by ADHD. Work together to identify and implement approaches that help manage the impact of ADHD on daily life.

This may involve setting reminders, using organizational tools, or establishing structured routines. Your active participation in these coping strategies underscores your commitment to the relationship and demonstrates genuine concern for your partner's well-being. By joining forces in navigating the complexities of ADHD, you strengthen your connection and create a shared sense of accomplishment in overcoming challenges together.

- **Establishing the Ideal Work Atmosphere**

Extending support into the professional realm showcases a profound commitment to your partner's overall well-being. Going the extra mile in the workplace for someone with ADHD can involve creating an optimal work environment. Consider helping establish an organized routine, offering gentle reminders for crucial tasks, and assisting in eliminating potential distractions from their workspace.

These actions not only showcase a deep understanding of the obstacles posed by ADHD but also reflect a sincere effort to contribute to your partner's professional achievements. By actively participating in their work life, you not only help them navigate the challenges associated with ADHD but also strengthen the bond between you, creating a foundation of mutual support and understanding.

Chapter Six

Enhancing Communication in ADHD-Affected Relationships

I n ADHD relationships, communication is the vital thread weaving together the intricate patterns of understanding, trust, and connection. When ADHD becomes a part of this intricate dance, communication dynamics take on a nuanced and often challenging dimension. This chapter explores how we can enrich and fortify communication strategies within relationships affected by attention deficit hyperactivity disorder.

Understanding that ADHD brings its unique characteristics—impulsivity, distractibility, and difficulty sustaining attention—provides the foundation for this exploration. Individuals affected by ADHD may find expressing themselves and interpreting their partners' messages to be influenced by the ebb and flow of their attention spans and impulsivity. As we navigate this intricate landscape, the objective is not merely to decode the challenges but to unravel the potential for growth, empathy, and strengthened bonds within these relationships.

Effective communication within ADHD-affected relationships involves more than the spoken word. It encompasses the subtleties of nonverbal cues, the art of active listening, and creating a safe and supportive space for expression. The aim is not to find fault or assign blame but to explore practical and empathetic approaches that can foster understanding, reduce frustration, and elevate the overall quality of the relationship.

Throughout this chapter, our journey will delve into proven strategies, real-life anecdotes, and expert insights, offering a comprehensive guide to enhancing communication in the context of ADHD-affected relationships. We will explore the intricacies of cultivating patience, navigating the ebb and flow of emotions, and adapting communication styles to align with the unique needs of partners affected by ADHD. By offering a holistic perspective, we strive to equip partners with the tools needed to bridge communication gaps and, ultimately, foster a deeper, more resilient connection.

Join us as we navigate the intricate landscape where love, communication, and ADHD intersect, striving to provide couples with the tools they need to cope with challenges and thrive, fostering enduring connections and a shared journey toward a more fulfilling and harmonious relationship.

Tool 11: ADHD Couples Communication

Picture a room with 1,000 TVs, with each TV showing something different. Now try and concentrate on just one TV without getting distracted.

–Damian DaViking Aird

In ADHD relationships, trying to stay focused on one thing is like attempting to watch a single TV channel in a room full of distractions. Folks with ADHD might find their minds wandering to different thoughts, or they could get easily sidetracked by external stuff, making communication a bit trickier.

Dealing with these challenges is crucial for good communication in ADHD-affected relationships. Being patient, understanding, and keeping those communication lines open are critical. Clear communication methods, setting expectations, and adjusting for ADHD-related issues can really boost how well you connect.

The quote's metaphor is an excellent way to picture the ups and downs of communication in ADHD relationships. It reminds us to bring empathy and work together to handle the unique cognitive stuff that comes with ADHD. In this scenario, the significance of effective communication cannot be overstated.

This tool delves into the art of crafting tailored communication techniques, recognizing that the typical methods may not fully resonate within the unique dynamics of ADHD-affected partnerships. Clear and concise expression takes center stage, emphasizing the need for articulating needs and emotions in a manner that aligns with the cognitive patterns of a partner with ADHD. Furthermore, the tool advocates for developing structured communication plans, offering couples a strategic approach to navigating discussions. By implementing these techniques, couples can transform their communication from a potential source of frustration into a shared strength, fostering a deeper understanding and connection that transcends the challenges posed by ADHD.

Communication in ADHD-affected relationships extends beyond the spoken word; it involves a deeper appreciation for the intricacies of expression within the context of ADHD. Recognizing the potential for information overload or distraction, couples are encouraged to embrace strategies that enhance clarity and focus. This may involve breaking down complex discussions into manageable segments, employing visual aids, or incorporating regular check-ins to ensure mutual understanding. The goal is to create an environment where both partners feel heard and validated, fostering an atmosphere of patience, empathy, and active engagement in the shared journey of navigating ADHD within their relationship.

Furthermore, the tool encourages couples to view communication as an ongoing process of refinement and adaptation. By regularly reassessing and adjusting their communication strategies based on feedback and experiences, couples can foster a dynamic and resilient dialogue. This adaptive approach recognizes that the needs and challenges within an ADHD-affected relationship are fluid, requiring a commitment to continuous improvement. Ultimately, this tool aims to equip couples with the skills to transform their communication into a source of strength, understanding, and connection, navigating the complexities of ADHD with a shared sense of purpose and cohesion.

Tool 12: Active Listening Exercises

Active listening emerges as a crucial tool for successful communication, particularly in relationships influenced by the nuances of ADHD. This tool goes beyond theoretical concepts, offering practical exercises to hone active listening skills. Through the implementation of mirroring techniques, where partners reflect on each other's thoughts and emotions, couples are encouraged to deepen their understanding of one another. This exercise reduces the risk of misunderstandings and creates a safe and supportive space where both partners feel heard and valued. The power of paraphrasing is also explored, providing a structured approach to summarizing and clarifying information, ensuring that messages are accurately received.

Active listening exercises become a transformative practice, fostering understanding and empathy within the relationship. By incorporating these exercises into daily interactions, couples establish a rhythm of communication that transcends the challenges posed by ADHD. The deliberate act of acknowledging each other's perspectives and validating emotions creates a foundation of trust and connection. These exercises become more than just tools; they evolve into shared experiences that contribute to the growth and resilience of the relationship, offering couples a practical and tangible means to navigate the intricacies of communication in the context of ADHD.

Moreover, the tool emphasizes the role of patience and intentionality in active listening, encouraging couples to approach these exercises with a genuine curiosity about their partner's experiences. The goal is to foster an environment where both individuals feel seen and understood, building a robust foundation of connection that withstands the unique challenges of ADHD. As couples commit to these active listening exercises, they embark on a journey of mutual discovery, strengthening their bond and enriching their relationship with the depth that active and empathetic communication can bring.

Healthy Strategies

Understanding the specific difficulties is the first step toward successful co-existence. Instead of attributing actions to a lack of willpower, it is crucial to recognize the characteristics of ADHD and avoid misunderstandings. For example, when you forget to buy bread for the umpteenth time, it is essential to understand that it is not a lack of interest but a difficulty associated with the disorder. As we mentioned, having that empathetic capacity to put yourself in the other person's shoes is necessary.

An active involvement in the couple's therapeutic process is essential. Accompanying the person with ADHD to appointments, asking the specialist questions, and being an integral part of the process demonstrates valuable commitment. Additionally, finding emotional support to express frustrations or annoyances resulting from uncomfortable situations in communication can strengthen the emotional connection in the relationship.

In my own experience, I have learned that organization is key. Using tools such as whiteboards, shared calendars, or agendas helps to structure daily routines, facilitating the achievement of objectives. Anything to help you get organized.

Acting as a model of active listening, choosing quiet moments to communicate, and reinforcing routines are helpful practices to improve coexistence. Empathy and understanding are essential, and I have found that communication improves significantly by openly sharing my feelings and experiences. I learned that, despite the difficulties, working together on mutual understanding and managing routines can lead to a more harmonious and satisfying coexistence.

Take Care of Your Mental Health

Remember that being well is essential to providing well-being to the other person in a relationship; it is necessary for self-care and mental health. This fundamental principle is often overlooked amid daily demands and responsibilities. The maelstrom of reality can catch you; sometimes, you lose focus on how important it is to be healthy. Fill your cup before trying to fill someone else's.

Maintaining good mental health and practicing self-care benefits the individual and has a direct impact on the quality of the relationship. When we are emotionally and mentally balanced, we can offer our partners more substantial and understanding support. Emotional stability allows stress, tensions, and conflicts to be managed more effectively, creating an environment conducive to open communication and joint problem-solving.

Taking care of yourself is not selfishness. If we neglect ourselves, our ability to provide emotional support and understanding to our partner will likely be compromised. It's like oxygen on an airplane: Before helping others, it's essential to make sure you have enough for yourself.

Mental health and self-care also play a crucial role in preventing emotional burnout. When we burn out, our ability to be patient, empathetic, and understanding is severely affected. Self-reflection, setting healthy boundaries, and regularly practicing activities that promote personal well-being are essential components of maintaining a solid emotional foundation in a relationship.

Tool 13: Let Your Partner Know You're There, Too

In the relationships impacted by ADHD, partners often find themselves grappling with the need to stand up and make their presence notable. This tool recognizes the potential for one partner's challenges with ADHD to overshadow the relationship, leading to feelings of isolation for the other. It advocates for intentional moments of connection to counteract this imbalance. Couples are encouraged to create dedicated quality time, express appreciation, and engage in shared activities that emphasize the togetherness inherent in their partnership.

Standing up and making one's presence notable becomes an active and ongoing practice within the relationship. This involves expressing emotional support and participating in the partner's daily activities with ADHD. By engaging in shared responsibilities and moments of joy, couples cultivate a sense of partnership that extends beyond the challenges of ADHD. Additionally, this tool explores the importance of communication in letting your partner know you are there. Expressing feelings, concerns, and needs contributes to the mutual understanding that underpins a resilient and supportive relationship.

Furthermore, the tool delves into creating a safe space for expression, where both partners feel free to communicate their needs and vulnerabilities. This involves fostering an environment where open dialogue is encouraged, free from judgment or expectation. By standing up and actively participating in the relationship, couples strengthen the foundations of their connection, allowing both partners to feel valued and supported amidst the complexities of ADHD. Ultimately, this tool serves as a reminder that acknowledging and actively participating in the relationship is a reciprocal process, contributing to the overall health and resilience of the partnership.

Giving and Receiving Support in Couple Relationships

Giving and receiving support are essential for the health and stability of these bonds. Offering a net of emotional safety and trust, these elements strengthen the connection between two individuals. Providing and receiving support in moments of vulnerability creates an environment conducive to the open expression of emotions and also contributes to building trust. That's what it's about when we talk about the essential foundation for the growth of the relationship.

On a broader level, we talk about supporting each other in difficult times but always promoting the personal development of our partner, ourselves, and the couple. By encouraging each individual's growth, you foster an environment where both can flourish and achieve their goals. When used well, this process strengthens the emotional connection and consolidates a solid foundation for facing life's challenges.

Understanding ADHD, embracing it, and working to improve your life will be key to long-term success. Trust and willingness to support others create a space conducive to open and deep communication. The couple becomes a refuge where thoughts, feelings, and concerns can be shared without fear of criticism, thus cultivating a deeper mutual understanding.

Tool 14: Conflict Resolution

Medication is the most efficient way to jump-start treatment, but it does not effectively treat ADHD in marriages without the addition of behavioral changes. These changes must be voluntary. No matter how much a non-ADHD spouse may want to, she can't make her spouse do certain things like be more organized or more attentive. Furthermore, these changes must come from both partners. –Melissa Orlov

Conflict is an inherent aspect of any relationship, and within the context of ADHD-affected partnerships, addressing and resolving conflicts constructively becomes paramount. This tool explores the transformative power of the apology as a strategic means of conflict resolution. It guides couples through techniques for delivering sincere apologies, understanding the impact of actions, and rebuilding trust. By embracing the power of apology, couples can turn conflicts into opportunities for growth, healing, and strengthened bonds. This tool empowers partners to navigate challenges gracefully, fostering a resilient and supportive partnership despite ADHD-related tensions.

The concept of the apology as a conflict resolution tool involves more than a mere acknowledgment of wrongdoing; it encompasses a genuine understanding of the emotional impact of actions. This tool encourages couples to communicate openly and honestly during conflict, expressing their feelings and perspectives. The act of apologizing becomes an opportunity for both partners to practice empathy, recognizing the unique challenges posed by ADHD and the potential emotional toll of conflicts. By fostering a culture of sincere apologies, couples cultivate an environment where mistakes are viewed as opportunities for growth rather than sources of discord.

Apologizing without a sincere intention to make amends raises fundamental questions about the purpose and authenticity of our actions. Apologies, in their most genuine essence, go beyond simple words. They represent an emotional and ethical commitment to recognizing having caused harm or discomfort to another person. If apologies lack the genuine intention to change, they could become mere empty acts, lacking meaning and devoid of the ability to restore trust in the relationship.

The true essence of an apology involves deep internal examination and an active willingness to correct the behavior that caused the harm. If this intention to change is absent, apologies become a superficial exercise, incapable of generating a lasting impact. Additionally, apologizing without a real commitment to change can undermine trust in the relationship, as the other person may perceive a lack of authenticity and genuine commitment.

Apologizing should be accompanied by honest reflection on our actions and a sincere determination to change our behavior. Only when our apologies are backed by concrete actions and a genuine effort to improve can they become a catalyst for reconciliation and strengthening relationships. Otherwise, a lack of congruence between words and actions can erode credibility and undermine the very basis of trust in a relationship.

Furthermore, the tool delves into rebuilding trust after conflicts within the context of ADHD-affected relationships. It provides couples with practical steps to create a foundation of understanding and forgiveness, which is essential for moving forward. This involves establishing shared goals for growth, learning from past conflicts, and reinforcing a commitment to mutual support.

The Power of Apologies

The shadows of our past loom larger, and our missteps can hold more significant consequences, especially in ADHD relationships. The intimate nature of these connections, coupled with the profound personal investments at stake, creates a landscape where apologies become not just a requirement but a fundamental necessity for healthy relating (Johansen, 2023).

Despite shared inclinations, attitudes, and beliefs, differences inherent in ADHD-affected partnerships inevitably surface, becoming fertile grounds for troublesome friction. Hurt feelings become an inescapable aspect, afflicting relationships to varying degrees and underscoring the vital role of apologies in navigating the challenges unique to ADHD dynamics.

The question arises: What constitutes the most effective way to apologize and mend the proverbial fences in ADHD-affected relationships? Are some apologies more impactful than others, and can apologizing be refined as a learned skill?

The mere utterance of an apology may not always serve as a curative salve for the emotional wounds inflicted in the throes of ADHD-related friction. Apologizing in the context of ADHD requires a nuanced understanding of the specific challenges that contribute to conflicts. It demands a tailored approach that addresses the unique aspects of ADHD dynamics, considering impulsivity, distractibility, and emotional intensity (Johansen, 2023).

Post-fight, in the relative calm of a therapist's office, the heightened emotions that accompany ADHD-related conflicts subside, allowing for rational self-examination and flexible problem-solving. The clinical approach involves purposefully navigating the couple's past conflicts and understanding that these intense emotional episodes may repeat themselves.

Become an Expert in Avoiding Couple Conflicts

Conflict is an inherent component of any romantic relationship, and mastering the art of resolving disagreements is essential to fostering a robust and long-lasting bond. Let's delve into a detailed exploration of various strategies and approaches to improve conflict resolution in romantic relationships, emphasizing the importance of communication, timing, problem focus, active listening, "I" statements, seeking compromises, and considering professional support.

As we saw previously, the power of effective communication is the foundation stone of successful conflict resolution. Establishing a safe, open space for dialogue allows partners to express their thoughts and feelings without fear of being judged. This involves active listening, with both parties genuinely committed to understanding each other's perspectives. Through clear, non-confrontational communication, couples can bridge gaps and cultivate a deeper understanding of each other.

It is necessary to choose the right moment to address conflicts. Selecting an appropriate time and place for the discussion helps ensure that both partners are emotionally prepared and focused on resolving the issue. Avoiding impromptu confrontations reduces the likelihood of intense emotions and promotes a calm, rational atmosphere conducive to constructive conversation.

A good strategy for dealing with these conflicts is to focus on the problem, not the person. During disputes, it is essential to separate the problem from the person. Blaming or criticizing a partner personally can lead to defensiveness and make resolution difficult. By directing attention to the specific issue, couples can collaboratively explore the root causes and work toward a solution that benefits both individuals and strengthens the relationship.

First-Person Statements in ADHD Relationships

In interpersonal relationship contexts, "I" statements are valuable for constructively expressing needs, sharing emotions, and resolving conflicts. Empathy is fostered by communicating in this way, and space for mutual understanding is created.

In contrast, statements in the second person (using "You" or "Your") can often be perceived as accusatory, creating defensiveness and making problem-solving difficult. Instead of blaming, accusing, or generalizing, first-person statements focus on the individual experience and allow for more open, honest, and less confrontational communication.

Applying first-person statements in this context becomes even more critical, as it allows tensions to be addressed in a less accusatory and more collaborative way, thus promoting a deeper mutual understanding.

In the case of relationships where one partner has ADHD, associated difficulties, such as distractibility, impulsivity, or difficulty maintaining attention, can contribute to frequent conflicts. When we use "I" statements, these challenges can be addressed in ways that do not point fingers or blame but invite the partner to understand the experiences and emotions of the individual with ADHD.

For example, instead of saying, "You always forget our appointments," you could say, "I get frustrated when I feel like our appointments are constantly forgotten." This formulation emphasizes personal experience and emotions, thus encouraging a more open and less confrontational dialogue on the part of the couple. This way, we let our partners know how we feel without attacking them directly.

Again, empathy plays a crucial role, allowing both parties to recognize and accept differences in cognitive processing and emotional responses. Using first-person statements facilitates this process by highlighting how certain behaviors directly affect the person expressing their feelings.

Additionally, this approach can also be applied when the partner without ADHD seeks to understand the daily struggles and challenges associated with the disorder. Instead of saying, "You're always distracted," you could say, "I'm worried when I notice you're distracted. Can you tell me how I can help you during those times?" This formulation avoids accusation and opens the door to a more constructive and solution-oriented conversation.

The Importance of Negotiation as a Couple

Relationships are complex and dynamic, with inherent challenges that require careful negotiation skills. Negotiation as a couple involves active compromise, finding equitable solutions, and building bridges to deeper understanding. Let's explore the importance of learning to negotiate in the context of a romantic relationship.

First, negotiation fosters mutual understanding. In a relationship, each individual brings their own needs, desires, and perspectives. Through the negotiation process, both partners can express these aspects of themselves, leading to a greater understanding of the complexities of the other's expectations and aspirations. The open and honest communication that accompanies negotiation creates a space for both parties to feel heard and understood.

Negotiating efficiently helps avoid accumulated resentments and frustrations. In every relationship, disagreements and differences of opinion arise. The ability to negotiate allows these discrepancies to be addressed proactively, preventing them from becoming sources of resentment. Negotiation provides a means to find compromises and solutions that satisfy the needs of both parties instead of accumulating those conflicts, which generate pressure and explode from one day to the next.

Fairness and respect are fundamental values in any strong relationship. Negotiation promotes these values by allowing both parties to participate in decision-making. This collaborative approach ensures that each individual's interests and wishes are considered and respected. The resulting sense of fairness reinforces trust in the relationship, creating an environment where both parties feel valued.

Building trust is another crucial benefit of learning to negotiate. Reaching agreements through negotiation demonstrates the willingness of both parties to compromise and find solutions beneficial to the relationship. This willingness to work together reinforces emotional security in the couple and fosters a sense of collaboration and unity.

Negotiation can also create an environment of continued collaboration. Beyond resolving specific conflicts, negotiation generally sets a tone for the relationship. The willingness to collaborate on decision-making and address problems contributes to a stronger, more resilient connection.

Change is inevitable in relationships and life. Learning to negotiate helps address current problems and makes it easier to adapt to changes in circumstances or expectations. Flexibility in decision-making and the willingness to adjust relationship dynamics are key elements for long-term sustainability.

Finally, negotiation provides a framework for addressing problems constructively. Instead of seeing differences as insurmountable obstacles, the couple who has developed negotiation skills can face challenges with resilience. The active search for solutions and the willingness to compromise promote a relationship that survives problems and emerges stronger from them.

Chapter Seven

Reality Always Wins

W e'll see that each step becomes a negotiation between the desire for connection and the complexities that the condition introduces. It is a journey riddled with the demands of heightened awareness, where partners are called upon to navigate through distractions, impulsivity, and the ebbs and flows of attention.

ADHD introduces a set of dynamics that can manifest as distractibility, impulsivity, and difficulty with sustained attention. These characteristics can present hurdles in communication, emotional regulation, and overall relationship harmony. As partners strive to weave their lives together, the intricate dance between their individual realities and the shared reality of their relationship becomes apparent. This chapter seeks to illuminate the transformative potential of embracing reality within this delicate interplay.

This chapter goes beyond merely acknowledging the challenges posed by ADHD; it serves as a beacon guiding individuals toward a deeper, more nuanced understanding of their day-to-day interactions. In relationships touched by ADHD, being present is not just a fleeting gesture but a fundamental practice that paves the way for connection and growth. This chapter aims to cultivate a mindset that embraces the authenticity of the present moment, encouraging readers to confront the challenges head-on.

The transformative tools unveiled within these pages are designed to empower individuals to actively shape their relationships. Practical insights, strategies, and exercises offer a road map for navigating the unique hurdles posed by ADHD, fostering an environment where love, understanding, and personal growth can flourish. By equipping readers with the means to navigate today's reality, "Reality Always Wins" becomes a catalyst for positive change, sowing the seeds of resilience, empathy, and lasting connection.

By exploring the day-to-day intricacies, readers are encouraged to view challenges not as insurmountable obstacles but as opportunities for growth. The chapter seeks to instill a sense of agency, reminding individuals that they can transform their relationships by actively engaging with the realities they face. Let us immerse ourselves in the transformative power of presence, recognizing that in the tapestry of our shared moments lies the potential for deeper connection, profound understanding, and enduring love.

Tool 15: Be the Architect of Your ADHD Relationship Reality

When discussing ADHD in relationships, we discuss complex situations where couples navigate a landscape where the unexpected is the norm. Unlike neuro-typical relationships, where challenges can be more predictable, couples struggling with ADHD are thrust into an environment that demands active collaboration and intentional design.

Let us see the role of the partners in these relationships and conceive our work as that of architects of shared reality, emphasizing the importance of open communication, realistic expectations, and collaborative strategies in building a relationship framework that not only resists the challenges but also takes advantage of the unique strengths that often accompany ADHD.

You and your partner must engage in open and honest dialogue, revealing your expectations, fears, and aspirations. The deeper this relationship and the deeper the level of communication, the greater the chances of prevailing over the challenges that ADHD brings. This intentional exchange creates a foundation for understanding, empathy, and developing realistic expectations. Through these conversations, couples address the challenges posed by ADHD and discover strengths that can improve their connection.

To do this, it is necessary first to understand that ADHD introduces a level of unpredictability that can be challenging for both partners. Effective dialogue allows the couple to deal with the complexities of setting realistic expectations. We're talking about recognizing the unique dynamics of ADHD and designing strategies that accommodate its inherent complexities. As we saw previously, establishing structured routines and developing communication protocols are valuable tools that, strengthened as a couple, point to collaboration. In this way, the relationship becomes a road map that recognizes the need for flexibility while maintaining stability.

In addition to communication and setting expectations, couples are tasked with developing strategies to navigate the ADHD landscape successfully. This may involve implementing structured routines to provide stability in the face of impulsivity or developing coping mechanisms to manage the challenges associated with attention deficits. The collaborative effort to build these strategies lays the foundation for long-term resilience.

Attention deficit hyperactivity disorder presents a series of challenges in relationships, but it is crucial to recognize that it also brings unique strengths that can enrich the couple's dynamic. In this context, each member of the couple, with their strengths and weaknesses, can complement each other and work together to strengthen ties.

On many occasions, the person affected by ADHD can bring a significant dose of creativity to the relationship. Their ability to think outside the box, connect seemingly unconnected ideas, and find innovative solutions can infuse a unique spark into the couple's dynamic. This creative approach can inspire the couple to explore new experiences and perspectives, thus creating a more prosperous and stimulating relationship.

Spontaneity, another characteristic associated with ADHD, can add an element of excitement and surprise to a couple's life. Although routine and planning are essential in any relationship, the person with ADHD's ability to introduce unpredictable elements can infuse vitality and keep the flame of the relationship alive. The couple can learn to balance stability and excitement, taking advantage of spontaneity to keep the relationship fresh and dynamic.

In terms of perspective, people with ADHD often possess a unique way of seeing the world. Their ability to perceive details others may miss and their unconventional approach can offer a new perspective on everyday situations. This can be a valuable resource for the couple, as they can benefit from broadening their horizons and considering different points of view. Diversity in thinking can strengthen joint decision-making and foster an environment of mutual learning.

However, it is essential to recognize that these strengths can also come with challenges. Spontaneity can sometimes clash with the other partner's need for planning, and creativity can manifest as a distraction at critical moments. This is where open communication and mutual understanding come into play.

The Courage to Implement Changes

On the path to improving life as a couple, I understand the importance of moving from idea to action. Theory can be a guiding light, but the courage to implement significant changes transforms and strengthens the relationship. In action, in deciding, we forge what we want to do. It is through acting, in addition to thinking, that we achieve objectives. This way, we can improve our couple, family, and life.

First, a deep understanding of the situation became the spark that drove the need for change. We dove into the research, learned about the disorder's complexities, and embraced the idea that understanding is the crucial first step toward any meaningful change.

However, recognizing the need for change does not always automatically translate into concrete actions. This is where bravery comes into play. Implementing significant changes required letting go of the fear of the unknown and the comfort of an established routine. It was necessary to overcome resistance to change and embrace the possibility of a healthier and more enriching life as a couple.

Creating routines and structures was a tangible change we decided to implement. Moving from the idea that organization and planning could be beneficial to establishing regular schedules and to-do lists was a bold step. It was a daily reminder that the courage to change long-held patterns could lead to greater harmony and equity in our lives.

Communication became our ally in this process. Letting go of the fear of expressing our needs and concerns and acting courageously to share our thoughts strengthened our connection. Moving from the idea of "We should talk more openly" to creating a safe space for dialogue transformed how we face challenges.

Integrating visual strategies was another change we decided to implement. The bravery here lies in letting go of any associated stigma and embracing the idea that these tools could significantly improve our everyday lives. From sticky notes to shared visual reminders, these concrete actions became visible reminders of our mutual commitment to creating a supportive environment.

Adjusting expectations and patience also required an active shift in our mindset. It took courage to move from the idea that everything should be perfect to accepting and adapting to daily variations. Embracing flexibility was not a sign of weakness but a testament to our determination to build a strong relationship, regardless of daily challenges.

Ultimately, seeking professional help was the culmination of our courage to implement meaningful changes. Stopping seeing therapy as a last resort and instead embracing the idea that it could be a powerful tool for our growth together was a bold step toward a more robust, healthier future.

The lesson learned is clear: When an idea is combined with action, the potential for transformative change in life as a couple with ADHD is unlocked.

Tool 16: The Love Factor

Love, often considered an omnipotent force, takes on a transformative role in relationships affected by ADHD. Digging deeper into what constitutes "The Love Factor" reveals that it is more of a deliberate and ongoing commitment to meeting the unique challenges that ADHD poses with empathy, patience, and understanding. It is an emotion we feel in the depths of our being for our partner, and that sensation is the first driving force behind you being here.

When love is absent, things change radically, right? The reality is that without that deep emotional bond, the motivation to make significant changes to improve your partner's isn't there. It's not like when you feel connected, or love puts you in superhero mode.

In relationships with love, you are willing to make changes to improve your other half's life. It can range from changing your daily habits to rethinking your personal goals. Love is not just a passing feeling; it is like commitment on steroids, pushing you to strive for the well-being of another, even if it means some sacrifices.

When love decides to take a vacation, the willingness to make those significant changes disappears. Adjusting your life for your partner's well-being without that emotional bond feels more forced than a Monday morning meeting. It is as if emotional motivation has gone on a holiday and has no plans to return.

Love in times of ADHD transcends the traditional romantic notion and evolves into an action-oriented force that requires effort and intentionality. In these cases, love becomes the catalyst to foster resilience and stability. It is the unwavering commitment to weather the storms together and embrace the journey with twists and turns.

The essence of love between you lies in deeply understanding each other's experiences and challenges. Love compels couples to view their relationship as a shared journey, encouraging them to support each other actively in the face of ADHD-related obstacles. It involves consciously infusing daily interactions with expressions of affection, kindness, and emotional support. Love becomes a stabilizing force that anchors the relationship in times of chaos and uncertainty.

Faced with ADHD challenges, love is not a passive spectator; instead, it becomes the driving force behind practical strategies that strengthen the relationship. Regular expressions of gratitude serve as a reminder of the value each partner brings to the dynamic. Quality time becomes a means to forge a deeper connection, transcending the distractions that ADHD may present. Emotional check-ins, marked by genuine interest and empathy, allow partners to share their thoughts and feelings openly.

Fundamentally, without the foundation of love, all efforts to address ADHD-related challenges may be lacking. Love is the glue that binds practical strategies together, infusing them with meaning and purpose. It provides the emotional support necessary for the couple to weather the storms that ADHD can bring. In the absence of love, these challenges can become insurmountable obstacles.

When Love Ends

Ending a romantic relationship is never easy due to the complexity of the emotional bonds built over time. Intertwined with shared memories and experiences, these bonds create a deep, challenging connection.

Fear of loneliness, a significant investment of time and energy, and resistance to change contribute to the difficulty of taking a step toward separation. Additionally, social pressure, hope for future improvements, and shared identity in the relationship add layers of complexity, while fear of emotional pain and rejection can paralyze complex decision-making.

However, when love evaporates in a relationship affected by ADHD, things tend to get a little complicated. ADHD already has its bag of tricks, and when you take away the love, the mix can become even more challenging. Without that warm feeling of love, ADHD problems become like those annoying guests who never leave.

Struggles with communication, organization, and time management, which used to be comical misunderstandings, are now more like a horror movie without the funny part. Also, patience, that loyal friend who usually is there when there is love, can also decide to pack their bags. ADHD-related behaviors that might once have passed off as small eccentricities are now like those scratches on the record that you can't ignore.

The daily routine, which used to be a harmonious dance of shared habits, can become an uncoordinated stumble. Actions that used to be done with love and care are now more like mechanical tasks, and those little things that used to matter can fall by the wayside.

Communication, the hero that used to save the day, can now seem more like a broken game of telephone. The lack of love as a driving force can make talking about problems like trying to fix a radio with no signal. Words can lose their weight, and conflict resolution can become more elusive.

A lack of love can be like a dark cloud hanging over the relationship. Couples may wonder if they still share goals and values or are on different wavelengths. The sum of the challenges of ADHD can contribute to that feeling of being in uncharted waters.

But here's the reality: Not all stories end the same way. Some couples find ways to reinvent emotional connection like they're determined to give that complicated movie a second chance. Others, however, may choose to separate in search of individual happiness.

Although a lack of love can complicate things, there is hope for rediscovering, reinventing, or going your separate ways. Couples therapy and professional support are like lighthouses in the storm, guiding couples through turbulent waters and helping them make informed decisions about the future of the relationship. In the end, each couple's story is unique, and so is the journey through the challenges of ADHD.

Five Pieces of Practical Advice for Everlasting Love

The key to lasting love lies in never taking your partner for granted and constantly seeking creative ways to strengthen your bonds. This need to be consciously active takes on a special nuance. Spontaneity and creativity become powerful allies to keep the spark of love constantly burning.

In this sense, I present five unconventional but effective strategies to strengthen the love bond in a relationship affected by ADHD. These strategies break up the monotony and take advantage of ADHD's unique nature, transforming challenges into opportunities for deeper, more vibrant connections. Dare to explore these ideas and discover how creativity can be a shining beacon on the journey toward lasting and unbreakable love.

• **Journey to Creative Nostalgia**

In the journey of a relationship, we often forget the magic of the special moments that build shared history. The "Journey to Creative Nostalgia" becomes a shining beacon to rekindle the spark of love. Creating a "map of love" together, where every special place and moment is carefully marked, you embark on a journey through a time warp. This exercise is a tangible reminder of your shared connection and injects vitality and fresh energy into the relationship.

• **Sensory Surprises Calendar**

Routine can be the silent enemy in relationships. This is where the "Sensory Surprise Calendar" comes into play. Blind dinners with exotic flavors and movie nights with unusual textures are just the beginning of this unique strategy. By challenging the senses, unforgettable moments break the monotony and keep the relationship fresh and exciting.

The creativity and impulsivity inherent in ADHD find their perfect outlet in these sensory surprises, making them a playful and effective way to surprise and delight your partner. The key here is to transform the ordinary into the extraordinary, thus cultivating a connection that goes beyond predictability.

• Collage of Spontaneous Indulgence

A "Collage of Spontaneous Complacency" becomes a visual window to shared dreams and aspirations. Immersing yourselves in this shared creation project is like building a bridge between individual desires and shared dreams. The collage becomes a tangible reminder of shared goals through images, words, and symbols.

This exercise encourages open and creative communication, provides a visual framework that reinforces connection, and offers daily inspiration. The collage becomes a visual testament to the dreams you share, constantly reminding you of the individual and collective goals you are working together to achieve.

• Reverse Role Playing Games

Conventional role-playing games can take a fresh and creative turn by swapping roles occasionally. In "Reverse Role Playing," the couple can experience life from each other's perspective. This not only fosters empathy and understanding but also challenges pre-established dynamics.

Walking in another's shoes creates a deeper appreciation of each other's challenges and strengths. This exercise is fun and provides a platform for deeper understanding and renewed mutual respect.

- **Word Inventions Laboratory**

The "Words Invention Laboratory" is the perfect opportunity to build an intimate and exclusive language. Creating terms representing special moments or unique aspects of the relationship adds a layer of exclusivity and collaboration. These secret neologisms become a special form of communication that only you understand, reinforcing the feeling of a unique connection.

Furthermore, the creativity unleashed during this process nourishes the emotional connection and becomes a playful and shared experience that strengthens the couple's bonds.

Tool 17: My Personal Experience

The power of personal narrative becomes a guiding light through the labyrinth of challenges. A personal experience is another tool that encourages individuals to share their unique journey, creating a tapestry of stories that offer insights, inspiration, and connection. Individuals develop a sense of communal understanding by sharing personal struggles, triumphs, and strategies that have proven effective. Vulnerability becomes a strength as stories weave together to form a supportive network, reminding partners they are not alone in their journey. These narratives go beyond advice, offering a nuanced understanding of the diverse ways in which individuals navigate ADHD within the context of their relationships.

Chapter Eight

Think Big! Think Long-Term

I n this final chapter, we will explore essential tools that will serve as guiding beacons for couples, allowing them to navigate the ever-evolving dynamics of their relationships with resilience, commitment, and a mindset prepared for the challenges that may arise.

These pages will explore long-term strategies for strengthening and maintaining strong, healthy relationships. These are not simply temporary solutions but solid foundations that last over time. We will delve into the importance of continuous communication, providing practical tools and exercises for incorporating it effectively into daily life.

The key lies in the consistency of everyday behavioral practices. We will detail how these practices become beneficial habits and organically integrate into the daily routine, strengthening the connection between couples.

We will also address the vital task of celebrating shared successes and, equally crucially, navigating difficult times. We will recognize that achievements and obstacles are an intrinsic part of any lasting relationship and learn to use them as opportunities for growth and strengthening the bond.

This chapter seeks to provide theoretical information as well as practical examples and tangible tools. Through these pages, we invite you to embark on a journey of self-discovery and joint growth, where each page becomes a stepping stone toward a deeper, more satisfying relationship.

You will find inspiration and practical guidance to face life's challenges together, strengthening your connection with every step you take. Get ready to discover how thinking big and long-term can transform the dynamics of your relationship, giving you the tools necessary to build a resilient and nurturing bond.

Tool 18: Long-Term ADHD Relationships: The Art of Growing Up Together

This invaluable tool serves as a guiding light, shedding light on the art of maturing together within the context of a relationship. The journey to confront the distinctive challenges posed by ADHD requires a repertoire of virtues such as patience, understanding, and adaptability. At its core, this tool seeks to uncover various strategies to weather the storms and foster resilience and unity, portraying the relationship as an evolving canvas of mutual growth.

A fundamental aspect is recognizing the dynamic nature of ADHD. Rather than viewing it as a static obstacle, couples are encouraged to perceive it as a catalyst for continued development. This shift in mindset positions partners to meet challenges and collectively thrive, transforming their relationship into a resilient, flourishing entity that deepens over time.

It is about exploring shared experiences to make them the cornerstone of this journey. Partners are encouraged to engage in a deliberate exchange of thoughts, emotions, and experiences. This intentional communication lays the foundation for an environment where obstacles metamorphose into stepping stones, fostering deep connection and mutual understanding.

The transformative power of this tool lies in its emphasis on a shared commitment to learning and adaptation. Couples are urged to approach the journey with a willingness to understand not only each other but also the complexities of ADHD itself. Through joint learning experiences, partners can develop a language of resilience, creating a narrative that turns challenges into opportunities and differences into strengths.

The Changes of Life

The greatest discovery of all time is that a person can change his future by merely changing his attitude.

–Oprah Winfrey

The importance of accepting each other's changes throughout life as a couple lies in the ability to adapt and grow together. In a long-lasting relationship, it is inevitable that both people experience transformations on a personal and emotional level and even in their life perspectives. Acceptance of these changes becomes a fundamental pillar for the strength of the relationship.

Understandably, witnessing your partner's evolution can be challenging and sometimes even terrifying. Seeing someone you thought you knew so well transform before your eyes can generate uncertainty and fear of the stranger. However, it is crucial to remember that change is a constant in life.

We all experience modifications over the years; we constantly evolve. Take a moment to reflect on your own life. Are you the same person you were 5, 10, or 15 years ago? The answer is probably no. And the same goes for your partner. We face challenges and learn lessons throughout life, and our perspectives are shaped.

It is essential to embrace the idea that, although there are transformations, there are fundamental aspects that remain solid. The essence of the relationship, based on mutual respect, love, and communication, can remain constant even as both partners evolve individually.

Life, with its unexpected turns, takes us to new paths and opportunities. Accepting changes in your partner is an act of love and a way to enrich the relationship. Understanding that change is a natural part of existence, a solid foundation can be built that allows the couple to face the vicissitudes of life together, strengthening their connection over time.

Tool 19: Practice to Incorporate

This tool is a steady compass that guides couples on a journey to infuse positive relationship practices into their daily lives seamlessly. It underscores the paramount importance of a sustained effort to foster a prosperous partnership. This section is a testament to the notion that small, habitual actions taken consistently can have a profound influence on a relationship's health and vitality.

A central element of this compass guide is the introduction of practical exercises designed to integrate effortlessly into the rhythm of daily routines. These exercises transcend the conventional view of relationship maintenance, positioning them not as cumbersome tasks but as shared rituals that contribute to the very fabric of the partnership. From this point of view, they become more than just actions; they become the heartbeat of the relationship, pulsating with shared intention and commitment.

A key defense of this section lies in recognizing the transformative power of habitual behaviors. Couples are encouraged to adopt these practices as obligations and ongoing investments in their relationship's well-being. Consistently incorporating actions like daily check-ins for open communication or regular expressions of gratitude makes these practices second nature, weaving a tapestry of connection that remains resilient in the face of life's challenges.

The underlying philosophy is that these practices when integrated into the daily fabric of the relationship, create a foundation for sustained emotional connection and intimacy. Just as a compass points the way to navigate uncharted territories, these relationship practices serve as a trusted guide, guiding couples toward a deeper understanding of each other, fostering a sense of security, and ultimately contributing to strength. In essence, the 19th tool is an invitation to transform daily rituals into meaningful expressions of love, ensuring that the relationship not only survives but thrives in the ebb and flow of life.

Recognize the Difficulty in Incorporating New Habits and Customs

Human beings are creatures of habit. Our routines and customs give us a sense of stability and security in a chaotic and changing world. However, when faced with the need or desire to incorporate new habits into our lives, we encounter obstacles that can make this process difficult. From internal resistance to external pressures, a multitude of factors can influence our ability to change.

One of the biggest challenges in incorporating new habits and customs is the internal resistance we experience. Our brains are wired to seek familiarity and avoid change, making us feel uncomfortable or anxious about abandoning our established routines. This resistance can manifest in procrastination, doubt, or self-sabotage, making the change process even more difficult.

Life is marked by constant changes, from minor modifications in our daily routine to profound transformations that affect our relationships and life perspectives. Incorporating new habits and customs is an inevitable part of this process of change. Although it can be beneficial in the long term, it also comes with significant challenges and stresses. Recognizing the difficulty inherent in this process is essential to understanding the importance of being understanding and patient with both ourselves and others.

In addition to internal resistance, we also face external pressures that can make it challenging to incorporate new habits. These pressures may come from our social, cultural, or work environment, including unrealistic expectations, criticism, or lack of support. The pressure to conform to established norms can make us feel judged or misunderstood, making our change process even more difficult.

However, despite the challenges and stresses of incorporating new habits and customs, it is crucial to recognize that change is essential for personal growth and developing relationships.

Moreover, change within relationships cultivates a sense of adaptability and empathy. As individuals undergo personal transformations, they become more attuned to their partners' evolving needs and aspirations. This heightened awareness forms the basis for open communication, fostering an environment where both parties feel seen and understood. The journey of incorporating new habits, despite its initial turbulence, is a testament to the commitment to mutual growth and shared aspirations.

Regarding interpersonal relationships, incorporating new habits and customs can pose additional challenges. Each individual in a relationship brings their history, experiences, and ways of being, which can generate tensions when we try to integrate new habits or behaviors into the dynamics of the relationship. Resistance to change on the part of one or both members of the couple and differences in individual expectations or needs can create conflict and difficulties in the relationship.

Tool 20: Be Prepared for Setbacks

Knowing that there will be contracts is having the wisdom that recognizes a universal truth within lasting relationships: the inevitability of difficulties. This section is a sincere recognition that challenges are not mere occasional detours but integral components of couples' intricate journey. Beyond acknowledging this reality, the tool offers invaluable guidance for cultivating a mindset that transforms setbacks from insurmountable obstacles into opportunities for growth and resilience.

In essence, the tool encourages couples to perceive setbacks not as obstacles but as transformative junctures in their shared journey. Embracing challenges as potential catalysts for growth means partners can navigate turbulent times with a shared sense of resilience and mutual support. This shift in perspective becomes a cornerstone for weathering storms, fostering a mindset that sees setbacks not as signs of failure but as invitations to evolve and strengthen the bonds that unite them.

Practical strategies take center stage in this section and address key aspects of dealing with setbacks. As we already saw with problem-solving techniques, conflict resolution, and emotional coping strategies, couples have tools that transform challenges into opportunities for collective problem-solving. The emphasis is on addressing setbacks as a united front, with partners working collaboratively to find solutions that honor both individual needs and the dynamics of their relationship.

Fundamentally, the tool underscores the importance of celebration, not just of triumphs but of the shared ability to overcome setbacks. Celebrating the resilience shown during difficult times becomes a ritual of recognition, fostering a deep sense of achievement and strengthening the bond between partners.

You'll find that setbacks cease to be mere obstacles when viewed through the lens of shared growth and resilience. Instead, they transform into stepping stones, each one leaving an indelible mark on the couple's journey. Far from hindrances, these challenges become pivotal points of transformation, shaping a relationship that not only weathers adversities but emerges from them with newfound strength and resilience.

The Impact of Setbacks in ADHD Relationships

In any social revolution, there are times when the tailwinds of triumph and fulfillment favor us and other times when strong headwinds of disappointment and setbacks beat against us relentlessly. We must not permit adverse winds to overwhelm us as we journey across life's mighty Atlantic; our engines of courage must sustain us in spite of the winds. This refusal to be stopped, this courage to be, this determination to go on in spite of is the hallmark of any great movement. –Martin Luther King Jr.

If you notice that your partner frequently finds themselves dealing with perpetual lateness, disorganization, forgetfulness, and the overwhelming weight of responsibilities, they may be struggling with ADHD. This condition, particularly in adults, presents a variety of symptoms associated with attention deficit disorder, potentially impeding success both in relationships and professionally.

For many, maintaining a relationship is inherently challenging. This challenge is amplified when the partner has ADHD, leading to potential misunderstandings, frustrations, and resentments. Symptoms of adult ADHD, such as appearing distracted, easily distracted, and forgetful, can strain relationships, especially when the individual has not received proper diagnosis and treatment from an adult ADHD specialist.

These difficulties can cause even the most loving relationships to fail and fall apart. However, there is hope to build healthier, more resilient relationships by delving into the complexities of ADHD and collectively addressing the challenges to prevent relationship breakdowns.

Living with ADHD can create a feeling of being constantly criticized, scolded, or micromanaged, making people feel unappreciated and disrespected and, in turn, potentially causing their partners to feel ignored and alone. This dynamic sets the stage for a destructive cycle, where the non-ADHD partner may express dissatisfaction, leading to feelings of judgment and incomprehension for the person with ADHD.

Fortunately, it doesn't have to be a continuous cycle of discord. To transform a relationship into something satisfying, it is essential to communicate and make the partner understand the role that ADHD plays in daily life. Assistance is available, and the crucial first step toward effective ADHD therapy is understanding its challenges. With this awareness, individuals can learn to compensate for their weaknesses and leverage their strengths.

Conclusion

In these pages, we find ourselves at the intersection of reflection and anticipation, looking back at the winding path we have traversed together. This journey through the intricate terrain of love influenced by Attention Deficit Hyperactivity Disorder has been a tapestry of challenges, triumphs, and growth. As we say goodbye, let us take a moment to contemplate the lessons learned, the resilience discovered, and the deep connection forged. This conclusion is a nostalgic look at the footprints left behind and a call to action for the journey ahead.

Our exploration of the tools provided in this book has been a guided odyssey, and each chapter has been a compass guiding us through the complexities of relationships influenced by ADHD. From understanding the nuances of communication to overcoming setbacks and celebrating successes, the tools presented have served as lanterns illuminating the path to healthier, more resilient partnerships. As we reflect on these ideas, it becomes clear that the journey is not simply about conquering the challenges of ADHD but about accepting them as opportunities for shared growth and evolution.

Now, with the tools in hand and wisdom gained, the call to action is clear: apply, persist, and thrive. The conclusion of this book is not an endpoint but a launching pad for sustained commitment to the strategies provided. Relationships, especially those influenced by ADHD, require continued dedication, a commitment to practicing learned techniques, and a willingness to adapt as the couple grows individually and together. The call is to incorporate these strategies not as a temporary solution but as an integral part of the fabric of your relationship, weaving them into the daily tapestry of your shared life.

Expressing gratitude is essential to this conclusion: gratitude for your dedication to facing challenges head-on, resilience in the face of setbacks, and commitment to fostering love in the ADHD landscape. Your journey is a testament to the strength of the human spirit and love's ability to transcend obstacles. As we part, I wholeheartedly appreciate your trust in this exploration. The commitment you have shown to understanding and navigating the complexities of ADHD in love is the cornerstone of your growth.

To conclude, let this conclusion not be a farewell but a continuation of the journey. As you step forward, armed with new knowledge and a tool kit for resilience, may your path be filled with moments of connection, understanding, and lasting love. *ADHD in Love* is not just a book but a companion on your journey, offering ideas and guidance when the path seems uncertain. With gratitude and anticipation, let us carry the lessons learned and the love cultivated into the next chapter of your shared story.

Thank you for reading this book. I truly enjoyed writing it, and I hope the information and insights shared will help you improve and strengthen your relationships. If you found value in this book, I would greatly appreciate it if you could take a moment to leave a review. Your feedback means a lot to me and helps others discover the benefits of this work. Thank you for your support!

-Maya

References

ADHD and relationships: How to make it work. (2023, March 6). Psycom. https://www.psycom.net/adhd-and-relationships

ADHD and romantic relationships: Neurodivergent love and understanding. (n.d.). Additudemag. https://www.additudemag.com/adhd-and-romantic-relationships-neurodivergent-love/

ADHD complicates romance. (n.d.). CHADD. https://chadd.org/adhd-weekly/adhd-complicates-romance/

ADHD quotes about the neurodivergent way of paying attention. (2022, April 15). Everyday Power. https://everydaypower.com/adhd-quotes/

Alcedo, M. (2020, January 31). *These quotes about change will help you when times get tough.* Country Living. https://www.countryliving.com/life/entertainment/g5153/positive-quotes-about-change/

Barkley, Russell A. (2015). *History of ADHD. In R. A. Barkley* (Ed.), *Attention-Deficit Hyperactivity Disorder: A Handbook for Diagnosis and Treatment, 4th ed.* (pp. 356–390). New York, NY: Guilford Press.

Block, C. (2023, October 17). *6 ways to improve your ADHD marriage.* Sane Spaces. https://sanespaces.com/2023/10/6-ways-to-improve-your-adhd-marriage/

Brown, T. (2014, July 29). *ADHD quotes for information and inspiration.* ADHD Collective. https://adhdcollective.com/adhd-quotes-gallery/

Bush Bollay. (n.d.). *ADHD Awareness Month: 9 motivational ADHD quotes to keep going!* Tutor House. https://tutorhouse.co.uk/blog/adhd-awareness-month-9-motivational-adhd-quotes-to-keep-going

Can ADHD affect your empathy? (2022, September 11). Healthline. https://www.healthline.com/health/adhd/adhd-and-empathy

Compasión - Qué es, características, importancia y ejemplos. (n.d.). Concepto. https://concepto.de/compasion/

Dodson, W., M.D., & LF-APA. (2016, November 28). *"OMG, so that's why I do that?!"* ADDitude. https://www.additudemag.com/slideshows/decoding-the-adhd-mind/

Ellison, K. (2023). *ADHD love quotes.* Goodreads. https://www.goodreads.com/quotes/tag/adhd-love

Gaia Novarino. (2017). The science of love in ASD and ADHD. *Science Translational Medicine, 9*(411). https://doi.org/10.1126/scitranslmed.aap8168

Gutierrez Frutos. (2022). *¿Cómo afecta el TDAH al manejo emocional?* Conectandopacientes.es. https://www.conectandopacientes.es/blog/tdah/como-afecta-el-tdah-al-manejo emocional

Hallowell. (n.d.). *10 uplifting quotes to inspire introverts with ADHD.* LinkedIn. https://www.linkedin.com/pulse/10-uplifting-quotes-inspire-introverts-adhd-kyrus-keenan-westcott/

Halverstadt, J. (2010, June 17). *10 ways to save your relationship.* ADDitude. https://www.additudemag.com/save-your-adhd-relationship-marriage/

How ADHD self-awareness unlocks productivity and power. (n.d.). Additudemag. https://www.additudemag.com/self-awareness-adhd-brain-power-productivity/#:~:text=ADHD%20Self%2DAwareness%20Begins%20with

How adults with ADHD think: Understanding the neurology of ADD. (n.d.). Additudemag. https://www.additudemag.com/adhd-in-adults-nervous-system/?utm_source=eletter&utm_medium=email&utm_campaign=adult_february_2018&utm_content=022018

How to practice self-compassion with ADHD. (n.d.). Additudemag. htt ps://www.additudemag.com/self-compassion-practice-adhd-shame/

Indeed Editorial Team. (2022, October 3). *Emotional management skills: What they are and how to develop them.* Indeed Career Guide. https://www.indeed.com/career-advice/career-development/emo tional-management-skills

Johansen. (2023). *The power apology: It can repair the damage.* Psychology Today. https://www.psychologytoday.com/us/blog/a-new-gps-for-intimat e-relationships/202310/the-power-apology-it-can-repair-the-damage

Lee, C. I. (2021, October 18). *How to regulate emotions as an adult with ADHD.* LA Concierge Psychologist. https://laconciergepsychologist.co m/blog/regulate-emotions-adult-adhd/

Murray, A., Lavoie, J., Booth, T., Eisner, M., & Ribeaud, D. (2021). To what extent does emotional dysregulation account for aggression associated with ADHD symptoms? An experience sampling study. *Psychiatry Research, 303,* 114059. https://doi.org/10.1016/j.psychres.2021.114059

Myths and misunderstandings. (2018). CHADD. https://chadd.org/a bout-adhd/myths-and-misunderstandings/

Orlov, M. (n.d.). *The ADHD effect on marriage quotes by Melissa Orlov.* Goodreads. Retrieved February 26, 2024, from https://www.goodreads.com/work/quotes/13476106-the-adhd-ef fect-on-marriage-understand-and-rebuild-your-relationship-in

Overcommitment and ADHD burnout: Stop saying "yes" to everything! (n.d.). Get in Flow. https://www.getinflow.io/post/overcommitment-an d-adhd-burnout

Owens, Elizabeth, et al. (2015). Developmental progression and gender differences among individuals with ADHD. In R. A. Barkley (Ed.), Attention-Deficit Hyperactivity Disorder: A Handbook for Diagnosis and Treatment, 4th ed. (pp. 223–255). New York, NY: Guilford Press.

Quotes. (2020, September 10). *35 powerful quotes on the importance of emotional intelligence!* Beyond the Shop Door. https://beyondtheshopd oor.com/2020/09/10/35-powerful-quotes-on-the-imp

Renteria, Y. (2022, May 23). *Two different brains in love: Conflict resolution in neurodiverse relationships.* The Gottman Institute. https://www.gottman.com/blog/two-different-brains-in-love-conf lict-resolution-in-neurodiverse-relationships/

Roberts, W. (2022, October 10). *Let's talk about how ADHD impacts your relationships.* William Roberts. https://focusedmindadhdcounselin g.com/lets-talk-about-how-adhd-impacts-your-relationships/

Segal, R. (2019). *Managing adult ADHD.* HelpGuide.org . https://www.helpguide.org/articles/add-adhd/managing-adult-adhd-at tention-deficit-disorder.htm

Setbacks quotes (91 quotes). (n.d.). Goodreads. https://www.goodreads .com/quotes/tag/setbacks

7 truths about ADHD and intense emotions. (2018, February 26). ADDitude. https://www.additudemag.com/adhd-emotional-regulation-vid eo/

Sounderic. (2023, August 2). *Understanding ADHD and communication difficulties in adults.* Sounderic. https://www.sounderic.com/post/ understanding-adhd-and-communication-difficulties-in-adults

The ADHD-anger connection. (n.d.). Psychology Today. https://www.psychologytoday.com/gb/blog/your-way-adhd/2021 09/the-adhd-anger-connection

Visser, Susanna N., et al. (September 3, 2015). Diagnostic experiences of children with attention-deficit/hyperactivity disorder. National Health

Statistics Reports; no 81. Hyattsville, MD: National Center for Health Statistics.

Wood, K. M. (2023, August 31). *The impact of ADHD on relationships*. Confidently Authentic. https://confidentlyauthentic.com/adhd-on-rela tionships/

Printed in Great Britain
by Amazon